SPIRITUAL
PARADOX OF
ADDICTION

THE
SPIRITUAL
PARADOX OF
ADDICTION

The Call for the Transcendent

Ashok Bedi, M.D.

Rev. Joseph H. Pereira

NICOLAS HAYS, INC.
LAKE WORTH, FL

Published in 2020 by Nicolas Hays, Inc.
P.O. Box 540206
Lake Worth, FL 33454-0206
www.nicolashays.com

Distributed to the trade by
Red Wheel/Weiser, LLC
65 Parker St. • Ste. 7
Newburyport, MA 01950
www.redwheelweiser.com

First published 2017 in Mumbai, India
Copyright © 2017 Better Yourself Books & Media Pvt. Ltd.

This revised edition published 2020 by Nicolas Hays, Inc.
Copyright © 2020 by Ashok Bedi and Joseph H. Pereira

All Scripture references are taken from the *New Community Bible* (Catholic Edition), published by St Pauls, Mumbai.

ISBN: 978-0-89254-192-8
Ebook ISBN: 978-0-89254-685-5

Library of Congress Cataloging-in-Publication Data

Book design and production by Studio 31
www.studio31.com

Printed in the U.S.A.

Contents

CHAPTER 1

CHAPTER 2

CHAPTER 3

CHAPTER 8

Faith Restoration—Preparing the Soil to Sow the Seeds of Faith Restoration

CHAPTER 9

CHAPTER 10

APPENDIX A

APPENDIX B

APPENDIX C

APPENDIX D

APPENDIX E

Foreword
by an AA Member

I HAVE BEEN blessed with several decades of sobriety through Alcoholics Anonymous, its program, and its fellowship. Thus, it was with particular pleasure that I received an advance look at the manuscript of this book from Nicolas Hays, Inc. I immediately realized its teachings will have wide appeal to a group of members who have been largely without representation in AA's otherwise-excellent literature.

Alcoholics Anonymous was founded by American Protestants in the post-World War I era. Their efforts soon received the enthusiastic support of several members of the Catholic clergy. As a worldwide phenomenon, AA has grown to include adherents of Judaism, Islam, Buddhism, Hinduism, and other established world religions. Addiction respects no cultural or national boundaries.

Dr. Bedi and Father Pereira, however, here offer a voice for a large group of modern members whose spiritual preferences have not been as intimately well-served by mainstream AA literature.

I am talking about those of us who have understood our quest for higher consciousness in the language of the new age and more universalist beliefs. From the Beats to the Beatles, Western spirituality has grown to include a wide range of Eastern and alternative ideologies and practices. While we all reach for the same goals, disciples of yoga, meditation, pantheism, gnosticism, paganism, and a host of others on the roads-less-traveled have essentially had to adjust our expression to fit in and prosper in AA.

Dr. Bedi and Father Pereira describe a more open even more tolerant path, with proven techniques for embracing the spirit and the meaning of love, faith, and surrender. At the same time, they treat Christianity with a sympathetic approach to its core message that will call to the hearts of all readers.

The authors make clear that the Higher Power is equally accessible to those whose understanding of the quintessential spiritual experience—so critical to long term sobriety—is different from the more traditional vision of AA's founders over eighty years ago.

I have been extremely fortunate in being able to adapt my interior communication filters to embrace the language I most often hear at meetings. The important thing in AA is to learn "to identify, not compare."

This book and its observations and advice on sobriety are a welcome addition to the literature on addiction and should be applauded by all who appreciate the Twelve Steps of Alcoholics Anonymous.

It will also prove of inestimable value to treatment professionals and friends and families, those who share an interest in the mysteries and dynamics of successful recovery, and who often have a personal stake in that process.

Preface

by + Agnelo Gracias

Emeritus Auxiliary Bishop
of the Archdiocese of Bombay

IT IS DIFFICULT to write a Preface for a book dealing with a topic with which one is unfamiliar. This
is my predicament in writing a Preface for Dr. Ashok
Bedi and Fr. Joseph H. Pereira's book, *The Spiritual
Paradox of Addiction.* The path to recovery from addiction, which this book outlines, is an unfamiliar terrain
for me. I must confess that I have been very much out
of depth in reading the book.

And yet, I can only welcome it because of the
freshness and novelty of its approach to the topic of
addiction. The book starts with the surprising statement: "Addicts are often spiritually driven people." It
develops this by showing how addicts attempt to replicate spiritual experiences through the use of alcohol,
drugs, food, sex, gambling, and other modes of addiction. In other words, the transcendent drive implodes
into addictions to alcohol, drugs, food, gambling, pornography, etc. Using the legend of Faust, the authors
show how the addict submits to the devil of addiction

who then claims his/her life and intrudes on the life of the addict's loved ones. Making use of the same legend, the authors trace the path from addiction to redemption.

What addicts often suffer from is what the authors term a "Faith Deficit." To use their words: "Addicts have a great hunger for the transcendent coupled with a deficit in faith." They give different case histories to substantiate this. The book seeks to combine the AA 12-step program, the insights of Psychology, the techniques of Yoga, the teachings drawn from different religious traditions, and so on—harnessing them all to set free the captives of addiction.

The authors have had a tremendous amount of expertise in dealing with addicts. They have tried to encapsulate their rich experience in this book. May the book be of help to many—that is a wish and a prayer!

June 29, the Feast of
Sts. Peter and Paul

A Note

From Dr. Ashok Bedi, M.D.

O**N A RECENT** visit to the Kripa Foundation in Mumbai, India, I had a fruitful dialogue with my friend Father Joe Pereira. He is the Founder and Managing Trustee of the foundation, which offers wonderful services for treating addicts and people living with HIV-AIDS. My wife Usha and I had a discussion over dinner with Father Joe about the process of addiction and the obstacles to recovery. He observed that in his experience, addicts have a "faith deficit." Understanding and attending to such faith deficits could have a substantial impact on rekindling the sobriety process. Father Joe and I had discussed this matter on and off for several years. Usha suggested during this conversation that we commit our ideas to paper. This set in motion the collaboration represented in this book. Usha is my soul-guide and she inspired Father Joe and me to undertake this opus.

I work as a Jungian psychoanalyst in Milwaukee, Wisconsin. Once a week, I present a lecture to the patients at the 155-year-old Aurora Psychiatric Hospital's Dewey Center for Addiction and Recovery. It has a certain healing energy about it. Every Thursday afternoon, come rain or shine, I walk from my office to the Dewey Center to present my lecture on the spiritual and psychological aspects of the recovery process.

Aurora Psychiatric Hospital has hundreds of patients with varying diagnoses and a large number of staff members. Over the last 40 years, I have made several interesting observations on this campus. The staff is generally kind but burnt out by caretaker fatigue. Most patients are depressed when they arrive and sad when they leave. One group of patients in particular has always drawn my attention. They are loud, garrulous and generally obnoxious, often smoking outside the non-smoking zone. However, after several weeks they become joyful, engaged, and greet me warmly. They are the addicts. They often come up to me and say that they have found my guidance about engaging the spirit extremely helpful; it gives them feelings of hope. Something in the content of my talks clicks with these addicts, rebooting their recovery, and leading to sobriety and eventually a spiritual awakening.

The dinner discussion with Father Joe and Usha solved the puzzle. It has been my long-term clinical observation that addicts are highly spiritual individuals. Father Joe's observation that these individuals may have a faith deficit led me to understand the paradox of addicts with a powerful spiritual drive but a faith deficit in their ego. The result is an implosion leading to addiction. *The Spiritual Paradox of Addiction* is our shared understanding of this paradox and of how to untangle its mystery. It is an attempt to help rekindle the urge for recovery and sobriety by way of bringing about a spiritual awakening in addicts—and to help them claim a conscious, loving connection with the grace of the divine.

Father Joe likes the Latin phrase *"Vocatus atque non vocatus, Deus advenit,"* which loosely translates as "Bidden or unbidden, God is present." The goal of recovery, sobriety and spirituality is to make a conscious, living connection with the sacred through faith restoration. Join us in exploring this restorative process as it has worked in our lives and in the lives of the patients that we have been privileged to serve.

A Note

From Rev. Joseph H. Pereira

IN MY PASTORAL life as a Roman Catholic priest since 1967, my focus of attention gradually shifted to the suffering and marginalized individuals called alcoholics. Providentially I was posted at a parish in Mumbai (then Bombay) as an assistant pastor. It was in this same parish that Alcoholics Anonymous in India began. Harry Mathias, a congregant of Our Lady of Victories Church, Mahim, read an advertisement in a newspaper from an AA member visiting Delhi and offering help to suffering alcoholics. Harry M., as he is now known, underwent the AA program himself and gratefully began spreading its message throughout India. Many would make their way to these meetings in a state of intoxication. As a young priest, I took special interest in spending time with them both during and after the meetings.

My interest kept growing after my transfer to the Cathedral of the Holy Name, the headquarters of the Catholic Archdiocese of Bombay. In the heart of the city, surrounded with many five-star hotels, I discovered tourists who were victims of both alcohol and prostitution. I reached out and received many of them in the open meetings of the AA in the church premises. In 1981, I was given pastorship of a parish at Bandra—a suburb infamous for its alcoholics and drug addicts. At the same time Mother Teresa's foundation in Mumbai, *Asha-Daan* (Gift of Hope), was receiving many dying and destitute people off the streets. Some of them had hit rock bottom from misuse of substances.

Eventually I requested my Archbishop to permit me to take in such people for treatment of addiction. Together with the referrals from *Asha-Daan* and many others from the streets of Bandra, I founded the *Kripa Foundation* to provide services to those afflicted with alcoholism and drug addiction. The inspiration and the encouragement of Mother Teresa—whose nuns struggled to cope with the numbers of suffering alcoholics who came their way—contributed immensely to Kripa's initiation and growth.

With these humble beginnings in a church annex, the message of recovery based on the AA program has spread across India and beyond with the vision of a global healing presence. The journey of the alcoholic-addict into recovery has been a mystery to many of us in the helping professions. It is well known that the early attempts by Dr. William Duncan Silkworth

[1873–1951], the American specialist in the treatment of alcoholism—and Carl Gustav Jung [1875–1961], Swiss psychiatrist and psychoanalyst—and men of religion such as Frank Buchman [1878–1991], founder of the Oxford Group—all contributed to the message of AA. At Kripa we have continued to explore the wisdom of the 12-Step Recovery Program. The golden thread of AA is the spiritual dimension of healing. Many have found the answer ultimately in a "conversion-experience" similar to that of AA's co-founder Bill W. [William Griffith Wilson, 1895–1971].

And yet, as discussed in the paper published by the American psychiatrist and advocate of AA, Harry Tiebout, one has to discern whether this experience is authentic. In his study of the people in AA, Dr. Tiebout discovered two categories of individuals who claim to have "turned their will and life over to the care of God" as stated in the third step in the 12-Step Program. Alas, for many it is not the "total surrender" as recommended, but only compliance. For them, total surrender is a challenge that sometimes ends in ego exhaustion. Numerous stories of people who carried their gift of recovery in a too-fragile vessel inspired Dr. Bedi and me to explore the authenticity of that "conversion experience" in order to achieve more effective interventions. Our work on this spiritual paradox is intended to help clients. In the words of Dr. Bedi, to help them access "the higher realms using sober, psychological, and spiritual paradigms—in other words, the restoration of faith via activation of the addict's ego-soul axis, the transcendent function," to result in a new spiritual attitude.

Kripa places great importance on the psychospiritual and psycho-social dimensions of healing addiction as found within the 12-Step Program. However, to aid in the authenticity of both surrender and adherence, we introduced a psychosomatic dimension through the teaching of Yogacharya B.K.S. Iyengar, one of the world's foremost yoga teachers (died in 2014) and considered by many as the "father of modern yoga." This spiritual dimension was already present in the 12-Step Program through the word "meditation" found in the eleventh step: "Sought through Prayer and Meditation to improve our conscious contact with God, as we understood Him, praying only for the knowledge of His will for us and the power to carry that out." As Guruji Iyengar described in a speech he gave at the 25th anniversary of Kripa: "Kripa Foundation teaches you how to combine the intellect of the head with the intelligence of the heart, so that the heart and the head are blended together, so that a human being lives as a human being."

The "Faith Factor" has now become an acknowledged component of healing and not just a placebo as some agnostic caregivers would call it. There is a genuine struggle in a suffering alcoholic. While keeping to the principle of HOW (Honesty, Open-mindedness and Willingness), an addict can benefit a great deal by reading some real-life experiences of genuine "conversions." Role models are important in recovery.

Along with such case studies, this book will also take a look at the findings of neuroscience that are acknowledging the role of meditation in healing. This book will therefore be a blend of science and faith. It will be a saga of human effort and the mighty power of God's grace. This paradox is explained by Saint Paul as: "virtue is made strong in weakness ... when you are weak, you are strong ... because My Grace is enough for you." Carl Jung echoed the apostle in his formula: "*Spiritus* (God's Grace) *contra* (against) *Spiritum* (alcoholic spirits)." This idea is carried on through the work of Dr. Bedi and myself. Kripa means "God's Grace."

To Our Readers

THE SUGGESTIONS IN this book may be used to complement your treatment program under the auspices and guidance of qualified addiction treatment specialists—and not in lieu of recommended treatment. For the sake of opening our ideas to the widest possible readership, we have omitted footnotes and academic citations. Readers who wish to delve more deeply into the subjects touched upon in the book can find more material in the bibliography, which includes the numerous sources that inspired and informed the authors. (Some of these are called out by numbers in parenthesis in the text.) We encourage people to use their own religious and spiritual traditions to engage the spiritual dimension of recovery.

Chapter 1

Spiritual Cravings of the Addict

ADDICTS ARE OFTEN spiritually driven people. Whether or not they are conscious of this or not, they are always seeking experiences that transcend the ordinary and mundane to claim access to the mystery of life beyond consciousness. They are seeking a variety of experiences well-recorded by mystics and elegantly summarized by William James in his classic thesis, *The Varieties of Religious Experience*. James defined religion as the feelings, acts and experiences of individuals that help them connect with whatever they may consider the divine. James referenced Tolstoy, who considered life to be meaningless if it took only finite existence into account. Beyond the reasoning intellect, faith explores and embraces the infinite which adds growth and meaning to life.

For James, one is converted when previously peripheral religious ideas take a central place in one's life and become a habitual center of energy. When cold ideas turn hot, they re-crystallize our consciousness. When the subconscious leads, the better self directs our personality. In this act of yielding to a higher power we give ourselves over to the new life, making this deeper self the center of a new personality. Following this line, Carl Jung, when counselling his patient Rowland Harrington, prescribed that he needed a sort of a religious or conversion experience to establish his sobriety. Jung's insight became a significant foundation of the 12-Step Program, which emphasizes the powerlessness of the addict over his disease and the need to turn it over to whatever Higher Power the addict understands. It's a psychology of surrender, which in Jung's terms means establishing a bridge from the ego to the self or the soul.

Addicts attempt to replicate spiritual experiences through the use of alcohol, drugs, food, sex, gambling and other modes of addiction. All addictive behaviors eventually lead to one of the three modes of connecting with the Spirit. Addicts getting high with uppers are trying to reach higher consciousness or a connection with the Spirit. By using downers, they attempt to descend into the soul and experience their own depths. The third approach is through the use of psychedelics to experience creative states of consciousness in an attempt to engage the mystery of the Spirit. Such states have been described as experiences of non-ordinary modes of consciousness.

If an addict learns to engage with the Spirit directly,

his addiction detours. He or she is able to gain a spiritual experience—or a deeper, higher or more creative state of consciousness. That is one of the key principles behind the 12-Step Program: restoring a connection with the Higher Power. The contemplative practices discussed in this book represent various modes of faith restoration and reconnection to the sacred without the use of addictive substances or behaviors.

A Deal wih the Devil

The legend of Faust has captured the imagination of the world for several centuries. It is a story of the faith deficit of Western Civilization, a problem that has increasingly spread to the East—where faith has become an empty ritual rather than a spiritual engagement with the transcendent. There are many versions of the Faust legend but for our purposes we will use Goethe's *Faust*, a favorite of Carl Jung. This will be further amplified by a commentary on the work by Jungian analyst Edward F. Edinger.

Faust was an avid scholar and philosopher who, in mid-life, was depressed and on the brink of suicide. However, at the critical developmental crossroad, he had a choice to make about his path. He could have sought guidance from his soul and the divine spirit through prayer, reflection and faith. Instead, he regressed to his dark side, his shadow, and made a contract with the devil, Mephistopheles, to seek re-engagement with life, vitality, and the feminine—as symbolized initially by Gretchen, later Helen, and finally by the Virgin Mother. The choice to make a deal with the devil rather than the sacred is the embodiment of the spiritual paradox of addiction.

Certainly, Faust had considerable spiritual drive, but he lacked the spiritual apparatus to reach out to the Lord. His pact with the devil was for self-renewal. This is the story of every addict who makes a bargain with his addiction for the renewal of his spirit—regardless of whether the object of addiction is alcohol, drugs, food, sex, gambling, pornography, or codependency. But this comes at a price: one must *submit* to the devil of addiction. And that claims your life. Here is Faust's deal with the devil.

Faust accepts a wager with Mephistopheles. Mephistopheles promises:

> Then here in service I'll abide,
> Fulfilling tirelessly your least desire,
> If when we meet again upon the other side
> You undertake to do the same for me.

Faust agrees, provided he has an experience of total satisfaction.

> If ever to the moment I shall say:
> Beautiful moment, do not pass away!
> Then you may forge your chains to bind me,
> Then I will put my life behind me,
> Then let them hear my death-knell toll,
> Then from your labors you'll be free,
> The clock may stop, the clock-hand fall,
> The time come to an end for me!

Spirits versus Spirituality

All addicts make a Faustian arrangement to renew their life energy through a conract with the devil, since their faith deficit blocks them from making a direct petition to the sacred, the divine and the transcendent. Jung eluded to this in his letter to the co-founder of Alcoholics Anonymous, Bill W.:

> I am strongly convinced that the evil principle prevailing in this world leads the unrecognized spiritual need into perdition if it is not counter-acted either by real religious insight or by the

protective wall of human community. An ordinary man, not protected by an action from above and isolated in society, cannot resist the power of evil, which is called aptly the Devil. But the use of such words arouses so many mistakes that one can only keep aloof from them as much as possible.

You see, "alcohol" in Latin is *spiritus*, and you see the same word for the highest religious experience as well as for the most depraving poison. The helpful formula therefore is: *Spiritus contra Spiritum*.

Any bargain with the devil comes with a high price tag and dire consequences. Faust brings ruin to his lover Gretchen: causes the infanticide of his own child, the murder via overdose of Gretchen's mother, the murder of her brother Valentine, and finally the execution of Gretchen. This dramatizes the trail of consequences an addict leaves behind in pursuit of pleasure and the illusion of power. An addict leaves a trail of death, destruction, and fatal consequences for his loved ones.

> Gretchen:
> My mother I killed,

My child I drowned.
Was it not given us both, and bound
Thee too? Thee! No—I can't believe it yet.
Give me that hand! But it feels wet!
(Blood of her brother murdered by Faust)
Oh! Wipe it off! It would seem
There's blood on it.
Oh God! Whom did I hit?
Put up that sword,
I beg of thee!

The addict's loved ones must pay for his sins. This is a curious karmic tangle. Perhaps the sin of the loved ones is co-dependency, tolerating and thus enabling the dynamics of addiction. They may break this vicious cycle by detachment.

Buddha counsels in The Four Noble Truths that the cause of all human suffering is attachment and the path to freedom from suffering is detachment. Alcoholics Anonymous has adopted a similar perspective for the loved ones of addicts, counseling them to remember that they did not cause the addiction, they cannot control it, and they cannot cure it. But they can care in a detached but compassionate manner. Gretchen could not detach; she enabled Faust. She had to pay for his sins. She was seduced—as all co-dependent individuals are—by the charm and promise of affirmation of their self-worth from the distorted mirror of an addict's reflection of them.

The second part of Goethe's *Faust* lays out the road to redemption. Here Faust engages the realm of archetype and imagination. Jungians call this a process of active imagination whose purpose is to engage the mystery of transcendence through interior experience, rather than acting out without insight for self-gratification alone.

Faust Part 2 has strikingly different characteristics from Part 1. Part 1 is personal. Part 2 is archetypal. In Part 2, it is as though the events of Part 1 are repeating themselves on the level of the collective unconscious.

In his masterful interpretation of Faust, Edinger explores the path from addiction to recovery. The empire in which Part 2 is set is in disarray, a representation of the state of affairs in an addict's life. Faust's reflective consciousness now allies itself with the Emperor's to help establish peace, prosperity, and even reclamation of land from the sea for the benefit of the people. Although Faust still allies with the devil, he uses the alliance in service of higher good. This is akin to the twelfth step of AA.

Step 12: Having had a spiritual awakening as the result of these Steps, we tried to carry this message to alcoholics, and to practice these principles in all our affairs.

The final step of the 12-Step Program echoes the final prescription of the Faust legend. It offers a way of redemption from addiction to recovery. Reclaiming the sea as land for use by humanity is a way of moving from self-gratification to altruism. It is a message of service to others. While recovery begins as a selfish program, it must culminate in altruism and service to others and the community. For an addict, that is the only path to truly connect with the divine. It is the road to redemption. Without service, recovery can never be complete. An individual who has embraced long-term sobriety must continue to participate in a lifelong path of action, not only to sustain his or her personal recovery, but to support the healing of other addicts.

In Part 2 of *Faust*, the protagonist attempts once again to engage the feminine, beginning with an encounter with Helen of Troy. There are several attempts to engage with the feminine at gradually more spiritual thresholds. In the realm of imagination,

Faust dies and reincarnates several times—each time with a gradually deepening spiritual insight and the transformation of Eros from lust to spirit.

Once again, Edinger reflects on the spiritual development of Faust (and every addict that he represents). Gretchen murders her baby (Faust's child); the Boy Charioteer incarnation of Faust disappears in the flaming conclusion of the pageant; the Homunculus reincarnation of Faust crashes in flames onto Galatea's throne; and finally Euyphorion (like Icarus) falls to his death by soaring too high. This sequence outlines the recovery/relapse cycle typical for many in early recovery, before the addict is able to establish a spiritual attitude and a sense of interiority, fellowship, transcendence, and service to support the recovery process. Jung calls this process the "spiritualization of Eros": the instinctual Eros of the addict is transformed from addiction to spirits in a bottle to embracing the all-pervasive, omniscient, omnipresent, timeless Spirit in the Universe.

Faust's lust for the flesh of the feminine is eventually redeemed by his devotion to the sacred feminine, which rescues him from the clutches of the devil.

Here concluding Part 2 of Goethe's *Faust*:

Doctor Marinus
Gaze to meet the saving gaze
Contrite all and tender,
For a blissful fate your ways
Thankfully surrender,
May each noble mind be seen
Eager for Thy service;
Holy Virgin, Mother, Queen,
Goddess, pour thy mercies!
Chorus Mysticus.
All that is changeable
Is but reflected;
The unattainable
Here is effected;
Human discernment
Here is passed by;
The Eternal-Feminine
Draws us on high.

What begins as lust, seduction, and abuse of the feminine (Gretchen) culminates in honoring the Holy Virgin, Mother, the goddess, and the eternal divine feminine, whose grace and mercy draws the addict and every seeker from darkness to light, from the spirits of alcohol to the engagement of one's higher spiritual nature—and the highest of them all: the spiritual flow of the Universe, the Brahman. Note the similarity here to the language of the Third Step, the first of the twelve steps of AA that includes surrender to service.

> Step 3: Made a decision to turn our will and our lives over to the care of God as we understood Him.

A question now arises: if Faust did not have the faith deficit syndrome, how would he have responded to the temptation offered by Mephistopheles? Here again, Edinger's essay on the temptation of Christ offers a paradigm for how an individual with a sense of transcendence deals with such temptations.

Christ is confronted with three temptations by Satan. First: "If you are the son of God, tell the stones to become bread." Jesus answered, "Scriptures say, man cannot live on bread alone; he lives on every word that God utters" (Matthew 4:3-4). This Edinger considers as a temptation to materialism. Second: Satan asks Jesus to throw himself off a parapet, "If you are the son of God," he said, "throw yourself down. He will put his angels in charge of you and they will support you with their arms, for fear it will strike your foot against a stone." Jesus answered, "Scriptures say again, you're not to put the Lord your God to the test" (Matthew 4:6-7). Here the temptation is to transcend human limits for the sake of spectacular effect. Christ avoids this narcissistic inflation that comes from power. Third: the temptation of power and possessiveness. The devil takes Jesus to a high mountain, and shows him all the kingdoms of the world in all their glory. All these he promises Jesus if he would only fall down and pay him homage. Jesus said, "Be gone Satan, you shall do homage to the Lord your God and worship Him alone" (Matthew 4:8–10). God is one's highest value.

Obviously, Christ did not have faith deficit. This is in contrast to Faust who yielded to the Devil. This is the problem with the modern human psyche susceptible to materialism, narcissistic inflation, and addiction. The Faust legend adds one significant dimension to the resolution of the faith deficit. While Christ did resist the temptations of Satan, the biblical account left the feminine out of the equation. Faust, on the other hand, started with the exploitation of the feminine principle in his seduction of Gretchen; but his story culminated in redemption *by* the feminine principle as depicted in the final words of Goethe's masterpiece, "The Eternal-Feminine-Draws us on high."

It remains the urgent mandate for modern humanity to redress the historic exploitation of the feminine, including Mother Earth, the environment in which we all must live. It is essential for the survival of the human race and our very planet. Contemporary culture not only dishonors the rights of women in most parts of the world, but ruthlessly exploits the planet on which we live without mutuality and balance.

Similarly, addicts dishonor the feminine principle by bypassing the feeling function. They are oblivious to the impact of their behavior and choices—on their own feelings, and next, on the feelings of those who love them most.

So in that manner, the addict is the executioner of the feminine on behalf of the rest of us. He carries the guilt for the collective. In a culture intoxicated with materialism, narcissism, and the exploitation of the earth and the feminine principle, it is the addict who carries the proverbial Scarlet Letter "A." He embodies the shadow self of the collective and the culture.

Chapter Two

The Transcendent Drive

TRANSCENDENT MEANS EXCEEDING our usual limits by going beyond the boundaries of ordinary experience, beyond even all possible experience and knowledge, beyond comprehension and material existence. The transcendent drive calls for reaching out beyond the limited ego consciousness into the realm of our spiritual origin. It entails establishment of the bridge between our outer ego consciousness and our deeper soul consciousness. Once we are able to establish this bridge to our own depths, we are then prepared to engage the spirit or the universal consciousness.

The Hindus call this a connection between the personal soul (*Atman*) and the collective consciousness (*Brahman*). Jung's analytical psychology offers a template for making a connection between the ego and our soul. It does so through attention to our inner life by engaging with our dreams, synchronistic events, relationship tangles, our complexes or hang-ups, our medical and psychiatric symptoms, and our addictions. Rather than remaining our problems, these symptomatic behaviors become a bridge to the mystery of our soul and engagement with the primal spirit.

As noted, addicts have a great hunger for the transcendent coupled with a deficit in faith. They are like a powerful car, a Ferrari with a superfast engine but a blocked fuel line. The car sputters but does not speed on the highway. In other words, despite the addict's drive to transcendence, he does not have the faith apparatus to embody and engage his hunger. The transcendent drive implodes into addictions to alcohol, drugs, food, gambling, pornography, co-dependencies and, today, the Internet. These addictions give addicts a transient connection with a reality and consciousness beyond their ordinary experience, but do not connect them with their spiritual core or the deeper mystery of the universe.

The task of recovery thus involves acknowledgment of their high degree of transcendent drive—and assisting them to cultivate their faith. They may then be able to make an optimal connection with their transcendent function. Cultivating the faith factor to counter their faith deficit will be explored at length in the rest of this book.

By faith we mean allegiance to duty or a person, loyalty, fidelity to one's promises, sincerity of intentions, belief and trust in God, belief in the traditional doctrines of a religion, and belief in something for which there is no proof, especially a system of religious beliefs.

Faith Deficit

In our experience, there are several facets to the dynamics of the faith deficit that apply to people in general and addicts in particular. The first kind of faith deficit occurs in individuals who have doubts about the very existence of the mystery of the divine. They feel that they are hurtling along in time and space, rudderless, at random, with no cosmic order or mystery guiding their path. They feel that the world order is a reptilian, dog-eat-dog existence where survival is by chance, force, and cunning. This is a sad state of affairs, reinforcing the lowest denominator of human existence. These individuals feel motivated and empowered to fend for themselves, albeit in a primitive mode.

The second group of those with a faith deficit includes individuals who believe in the presence of mystery and the grace of the divine spirit, but feel personally unworthy to be the recipients of such divine grace. They have a distorted sense of self-worth. They feel inadequate and unlovable. Their early life circumstances and relationships may have been troubled, thereby distorting their perceptions of themselves, others, and the world around them. Traditional psychiatric research has attempted to explore the relationship between addictions and underlying or concurrent psychiatric disorders (11–18). Individuals in the second group feel like step-children of God. They feel excluded from the Garden of Eden.

This feeling, which some children have in relation to their parents, has archetypal roots. The scriptural context relates to the story of Adam and Eve who betrayed God's word by taking a bite of the forbidden fruit and were cast out of Eden. It also relates to the story of Moses, whose tribe was punished for betraying the word of God and His commands. God told Moses, "Get up, and go down quickly, for your people, whom you have brought out of Egypt, are corrupting one another. They have been quick to leave the way I marked out for them; they have cast themselves a metal idol" (Exodus 32:7-8).

Even Christ felt abandoned by his Father when he was crucified. At the ninth hour Jesus cried out in a loud voice, "My God, my God, why have you forsaken me?" (Matthew 27:46). Yet, the New Testament also offers a prescription for this feeling of unworthiness in Christ's assertion that the poor, the down and out, are dear to God. "Truly, I say to you, as you did it to one of the least of these my brothers, you did it to me" (Matthew 25:31–46).

This particular prescription is crucial for recovering addicts: unless one engages in the service of others in need, an addict's recovery is never complete.

In clinical observations, addiction specialists have noted that addicts are always struggling to exceed the limits of ordinary experience. However, they lack belief or trust in God and usually do not have a viable framework for religious or spiritual engagement. They often struggle with a black or white conception of spiritual matters rather than a fluid sense of the mystery beyond comprehension. This creates a perfect storm in their consciousness. On the one hand, they have a high sense of transcendence. They are intrigued about experiences beyond what is deemed possible. But, on the other hand, they lack the mental apparatus for a belief system to help them engage their sense of transcendence.

To resolve this dilemma, they resort to addictions as a quick and easy road to transcendence—with all the consequences that come from this deal with the devil.

The task of addiction treatment, therefore, involves

recognition of the addict's high level of transcendent drive, and his or her simultaneous faith deficit. Treatment should focus on assisting addicts with cultivating their faith dynamic. The 12-Step Program promoted by Alcoholics Anonymous is one proven method of accomplishing that goal. This book will amplify supplemental methods for cultivation of faith to attend to the incarnation and embodiment of the transcendent function.

CASE EXAMPLE: WALTER'S ANGST

Walter is 70 years old and professionally successful, a recovering alcoholic for over 45 years. In spite of a solid recovery, business success, and community affirmation for his leadership and service to AA, he struggled with chronic anxiety and always second-guessed his decisions. He made sound and sober personal and professional decisions but always doubted himself. He often stayed up late with worry and/or woke up repeatedly during the night to obsess over the choices made. Psychotherapy revealed that he did not trust himself and prayed often to seek divine guidance.

Analysis of his childhood uncovered an

extremely critical and narcissistic mother and an ineffective father who could not protect him from his mother's demands. This negative mother complex became a block in his connection with the divine. He remembered an incident at his mother's deathbed. Her last request was that he sing her a song. When he sang her favorite song, her only remark was, "You did not make a single mistake!" It shattered his faith in himself, leading him to believe he was inadequate, unlovable, and unworthy of receiving the grace and the blessings of the Divine. The mother complex had taken the place of the Higher Power.

With the help of the 12-Step Program, augmented by psychotherapy, he gradually resolved the mother complex that had all along blocked faith in himself and his sense of self-worth. He established the pyramid of sobriety: God first, Walter second, and mother and everyone else later.

So how do we cultivate healthy relations with the mystery of the divine? Carl Jung struggled with this issue. He sank into depression after breaking with his mentor, Sigmund Freud, and endured isolation from his analytic peers. In this encounter with the unconscious, his dark night of the soul, he felt alone, abandoned, unworthy of the ministering of a mentor, friendship of his peers, and the benevolence of the divine. He struggled in isolation during his professional exile to transcend this sense of orphanhood and unworthiness and connect with the source, the *Brahman*, what he called the *Unus Mundus*.

Jung's journey is chronicled in his memoirs, *The Red Book* or *Liber Novus*, which became a new narrative and script for his life. He termed the process that guided him the "transcendent function," and the method he used to engage it was active imagination. This is a variation of the Eastern method of meditation with one major difference: in meditation, ego merges with the soul and the spirit; in active imagination the ego and the soul are given equal weight.

The repressed spiritual drive of addicts breaks through as addiction and shatters the ego, personality, and the ability to adapt in the process. In clinical experience with recovering addicts, we have found several contemplative techniques helpful in developing a healthy spiritual attitude. The central feature of these methods is the goal of establishing a bridge between the individuals' outer ego personality and the deeper center of their personality. Jung termed this center as the self or the soul, and Hindu tradition calls it the *Atman*. Once an individual has established a connection with her/his deeper, unconscious soul personality, the next step is to connect the soul personality with the Spirit, the *Brahman* or the divine. Gaining access to the collective source of life leads to wellness, wholeness, rejuvenation and revitalization of the personality. This is the transcendent function.

We will now explore the mystery of the cultivation of faith through the transcendent function, and how it manifests at the four levels of the recovery process.

Chapter 3

The Four Plateaus of Recovery

RECOVERY FROM ADDICTION involves a journey through four plateaus or stages that we will call Dry, Sober, Spiritual, and Service. We must begin by acknowledging that many afflictions of the mind and body, and our relationships with others, are a call of the Spirit through our soul. Its purpose is to usher us into higher levels of consciousness, that we may fulfil our spiritual purpose and program in this lifetime.

When we stray from our spiritual path and purpose, the Spirit sends us signals via dreams and synchronistic events, relationship problems, complexes or hang-ups, medical and psychiatric problems, including addiction. These indicate to our outer consciousness that we have strayed from the GPS of our spiritually purposeful path. If we listen to these memos from the soul, we have the potential to realign ourselves to our spiritual destiny. This knowledge of our spiritual purpose must also be put into play to guide our life towards service to the wider community.

Unfortunately, most contemporary treatment programs, grounded in modern psychology and medical science, are focused on alleviating symptoms. They are too busy to attend to the soul and the deeper instruction by the Spirit to realign us with our soul program, what Jung called "individuation," by which he meant becoming what we are meant to be.

Dry (and Detoxed)

Most addiction treatment programs have shown considerable success in treating intoxicated states, and involve safe and swift detoxification from substances. However, when the treatment focuses only on chemical detoxification, the addict is freed from the toxic effect of the chemicals. But he continues to operate out of a distorted mental apparatus. These are the "dry drunk" individuals, who, while no longer drinking or ingesting drugs, continue their dysfunctional attitudes and maladaptive behaviors.

"Getting dry" is just the start. Detoxification alone rarely constitutes adequate treatment. The provision of detoxification services without continuing treatment does not bode well for long-term recovery. Getting clean and sober is easy; staying clean and sober is hard. Many individuals have prolonged signs of withdrawal or a "protracted abstinence syndrome." Symptoms include disturbed sleep, anxiety, irritability, mood instability, and intermittent cravings. *The signs of protracted abstinence syndromes are not as predictable as those of acute withdrawal, but just as important to address in the early recovery phase.*

It is crucial that treatment providers instill hope and facilitate a sense of self-efficacy by letting the addict know that change is possible—but not without the person in recovery owning responsibility for it. Participation in Alcoholics Anonymous or other 12-Step support groups is immensely useful in helping people understand that they are not alone in their struggle with recovery, and that others who have "been there," have persevered, and are succeeding. The initial treatment experience of detox also provides an opportunity for addicts to be exposed to a variety of psycho-educational and holistic health experiences, which not only aid their physical recovery from alcohol or drug abuse, but also promote human development and spiritual growth.

Sober

Sobriety entails exploring and working through the personality flaws and character defects shaping the dysfunctional attitudes and mindsets that lead to addiction. The 12-Step Program provides a useful paradigm to systematically work through such character defects and minimizing the damage already done. This involves making amends to those we have harmed by our addiction, provided doing so does not harm us or them further. The fourth step helps us to make a courageous inventory of our personality flaws; the fifth step guides us to confess these to a trusted sponsor or advisor—which makes us conscious and accountable.

> Step 4: Made a searching and fearless moral inventory of ourselves.

> Step 5: Admitted to God, to ourselves, and to another human being the exact nature of our wrongs.

The sixth and seventh steps approach the spiritual source of our suffering.

> Step 6: Were entirely ready to have God remove all these defects of character.

> Step 7: Humbly asked Him to remove our shortcomings.

The eighth and ninth steps involve social obligations and protocol.

Step 8: Made a list of all persons we had harmed, and became willing to make amends to them all.

Step 9: Made direct amends to such people wherever possible, except when to do so would injure them or others.

The tenth step is the first of the action steps in maintaining daily spiritual fitness.

Step 10: Continued to take personal inventory and when we were wrong promptly admitted it.

In other words, while physical sobriety is vital, it is still incomplete in terms of achieving an enduring recovery. Sobriety by itself is like being dressed up with nowhere to go! Our sober self must now be directed by a spiritual purpose to complete our spiritual program in this lifetime. The Hindus call this one's *Dharma*; Carl Jung used the Greek term *Telos* to indicate our soul's purpose.

Spiritual Purposefulness

Restoring faith in the sacred dimension of life, in a higher purpose beyond mere survival, is essential for an enduring recovery. In the absence of a spiritual purpose, the addict's life energy recedes into addiction or other health, relationship, and personality problems. The eleventh Step of the 12-Step Program lays out the premise and method for the next phase of recovery:

> Step 11: Sought through prayer and meditation to improve our conscious contact with God, as we understood Him, praying only for knowledge of His will for us and the power to carry that out.

Many sacred texts insist that life is not about survival like animals but about a spiritual purpose through our understanding of God's will via prayer and reflection.

Jesus said, "Scripture says: Man cannot live on bread alone, but on every word that God speaks" (Matthew 4:4).

The prayer of Saint Francis of Assisi gives further guidance to seek the spiritual path:

Lord, make me a channel of thy peace—
That where there is hatred, I may bring love;
That where there is wrong,
I may bring the spirit of forgiveness;
That where there is discord, I may bring
      harmony;
That where there is error, I may bring truth;
That where there is doubt, I may bring faith;
That where there is despair, I may bring hope;
That where there are shadows, I may bring
      light;
That where there is sadness, I may bring joy.

Lord, grant that I may seek rather to comfort
than to be comforted;
To understand, than to be understood;
To love, than to be loved.

For it is by self-forgetting that one finds.
It is by forgiving that one is forgiven.
It is by dying that one awakens to eternal life.
Amen.

Once opened to the search for spiritual purpose,
some individuals feel smug about their "spiritual awak-

ening." This is not the right path. Many New Age seekers are so obsessed with the search for awareness of their spiritual purpose that their endeavor becomes a dry, intellectual exercise without a soul or action.

Carl Jung alludes to this problem in his four stages of the alchemical transformation of our personality. It begins with *Unio Naturalis*, awareness of authentic nature. This is followed by *Unio Mentalis*, knowledge of our personality structure and its defects, as echoed in the fourth and the fifth steps. The next stage is *Unio Spiritualis*, seeking guidance from God about our spiritual purpose. (See the eleventh step.) The highest stage of the alchemical transformation is *Unio Corporalis*, living our spiritual path in service.

> Step 12: Having had a spiritual awakening as the result of these Steps, we tried to carry this message to alcoholics, and to practice these principles in all our affairs.

Moses did not put out a position paper about the plight of the Jewish people; he chose exile and wandering for 40 years to guide his people. Buddha did not write wonderful books about his Noble Fourfold Path to enlightenment, but abdicated his role as future king.

He instead chose the life of a wandering monk to guide others. Christ did not publish political and academic articles to protest the injustices of the times, but bore his cross.

Every addict—as well as each one of us—must bear our cross, move from the horizontal concerns to the vertical purpose of our life, balance the mundane with the sacred and the profound, and live it. This is the stage of Service, the highest threshold of recovery embodied in the last step of the 12-Step Program.

The Healing Impact of Purpose in Life

One of the central tenets of analytical psychology is that the psyche has a purposeful trajectory guided by the archetype of the self. Emerging medical research now confirms the beneficial neurological impact of this purposive approach to mental health.

Alzheimer's Disease (AD) is one of the most significant public health challenges of the twenty-first century. Despite intense research, the agents causing AD remain elusive even as the disease is poised to overwhelm health care systems in the coming decades. Compelling evidence indicates that positive psychological and experiential factors are associated with maintaining cognitive function. Furthermore, novel neuro-imaging and recent clinical findings have shown that some of these factors confer protective benefits by reducing the deleterious effects of AD on cognition.

Having a purpose in life, the willingness to derive meaning from life's experiences, and possessing a sense of intentionality and goal directedness are all related psychological factors in well-being with positive health outcomes.

Systematic examination has shown that purpose in life is associated with a substantially reduced risk of AD and even mild cognitive impairment. In a recent study, researchers sought to extend these findings by examining the neurobiological basis of the protective effect on cognition for people who enjoy a sense of purpose in life. Participating in the study were 246 persons from the Rush Memory and Aging Project. The study tested the hypothesis that a higher level of purpose in life reduces the deleterious effects of AD's pathologic changes on cognition in older persons. It concluded that a sense of higher purpose does just that.

Every spiritual tradition has some framework to guide an individual in their *telos* and purpose-driven life. In Hinduism, one must surrender all actions to the divine:

> Surrender all actions to me
> And fix your reason on your inner self;
> Without hope or possessiveness,
> Your fever subsided, fight the battle!
> Men who always follow my thought,
> Trusting it without finding fault,
> Are freed
> Even by their actions.
>
> —*Bhagwad Gita*: chapter 3, para 30–31

And in Christianity:

> Your kingdom come, your will be done
> on earth as in heaven.
>
> —*Matthew* 6:10

Recovering addicts have been greatly helped by getting back to believing they have a "purpose in life." Psychiatrist Viktor Frankl recorded a beautiful story about a German addict. Unable to get a suitable job, he chose to spend his time riding a garbage van along with a friend. One day he noticed a broken toy in the garbage. He picked it up and fixed it. It struck him that it would be good to give the toy—now as good as new—to an orphanage. As he gave the toy to a child, he noticed the face of the child was full of joy. That gave him the motivation to gather, repair, and give away toys on a regular basis. He was eventually given an award of excellence by the German government. (Talk about a case of a "junkie" squeezing meaning from "junk"!)

Many addicts maintain their healing when they channel their gift of recovery towards a purposeful goal in life.

Service

As already mentioned, Goethe's *Faust* captured Carl Jung's imagination. At the entrance of his home at Bollingen was the inscription, *"Philemonis Sacrum Fausti Poenitentia,"* meaning "Shrine of Philemon—Repentance of Faust." In *The Red Book*, he traces his own transformation from Faust into the wise old man, Philemon.

The story of Philemon and his wife Baucus is instructive at this point in our journey. Baucus and Philemon, an old couple from the land of Phrygia, showed hospitality towards the gods and were rewarded. According to Greek mythology, Zeus and Hermes assumed human form and visited earth disguised as poor travelers. When they reached Phrygia, they looked for shelter but were turned away by everyone except Philemon and Baucus.

The old couple gladly shared the small amount of food and wine they had with the strangers. Baucus and Philemon realized that their guests were gods after noticing that the wine jug never ran out and that their poor wine was replaced by wine of the finest quality. Zeus and Hermes led the couple to a hill above Phrygia and sent a flood to destroy the land to punish the people who had turned them away. Only the old couple's house remained undamaged. Zeus made the house a temple to the gods and awarded Baucus and Philemon two wishes: to serve as priest and priestess of the temple and, when the time came, to die together. Many years later, when the moment of their deaths did come, Baucus and Philemon were transformed into trees with intertwined branches.

This is a tale of selfless service in relation even to strangers. In many traditions a guest is considered an incarnation of the gods. When we honor a guest even when they are strangers, we honor the divine. This is the conclusion of Goethe's *Faust*:

Doctor Marinus
Gaze to meet the saving gaze
Contrite all and tender,
For a blissful fate your ways
Thankfully surrender,
May each noble mind be seen
Eager for Thy service;
Holy Virgin, Mother, Queen,
Goddess, pour thy mercies!

This principle of repentance and redemption through service is embodied in the final step of the 12-Step Program as noted earlier.

Jung addressed the issue of the relationship between the individual and society, recovery and service, in his essay on "Individuation and Collectivity." The program of recovery must include a period of self-care and attention to one's inner work. However, this time is borrowed from family and society. Hence, the recovering addict must return this time to family and society—with interest. Here is Jung's formula for this bargain:

Individuation (Sobriety) cuts one off from personal conformity and hence from collectivity (including family and society). This is the guilt which the individual leaves behind him for the world that is the guilt he must endeavor to redeem. He must offer a ransom in place of himself, that is, he must bring forth values which are an equivalent substitute for his absence in the collective personal sphere. ... Only to the extent that a man creates objective values can he and may he individuate (get sober). Every further step of individuation creates new guilt and necessitates expiation. Hence individuation is possible only as long as substitute values are produced. Individuation is exclusive adaptation to inner reality (being oneself) and hence an allegedly "mystical" process. The expiation is adaptation to the outer world. It has to be offered to the outer world, with the petition that the outer world accept it.

The initial process of sobriety is a selfish phase. The recovering alcoholic/addict must focus on self-care, claiming authentic selfhood, and discovering and being true to her own nature. In the second phase of recovery the focus must shift to selfless altruism and service—to go from sobriety to spirituality. Only then can an addict truly heal. The design of the 12-Step Program concludes with service to family, community, and a higher good.

Jung proposed that individuation and collectivity are a pair of opposites, two divergent destinies related to one another by guilt. The individual is obliged to purchase his individuation at the cost of working for the benefit of society. Hence, the crucial value of service is that it is the final step towards enduring recovery. This principle applies to all forms of recovery. When we are gifted with health and well-being by the Universe, we must reciprocate. Selfish recovery is like a car without an engine, an ocean without water, a day without the sun. A further dimension of service is that we must not expect social esteem or affirmation as a reward. Service is expiation for our debt to society that makes room for our well-being and sobriety.

A recovering addict has walked the perilous path of addiction and the soulful path of recovery. He must share his wisdom about the dangers of addiction and the joys of the path of recovery with other addicts and society. Jung reflects on this issue with useful guidance:

I conceive it to be the duty of everyone who isolates himself by taking his own path (of recovery), to tell others what he has found or discovered whether it be a refreshing spring for the thirsty, or a sandy desert of sterile error. The one helps, the other warns.

The Healing Impact of Volunteer Activities

Included in Helen Lavretsky's excellent book, *Resilience and Aging*, is a fine summary of the resilience-building impact of volunteering and civic engagement. Among the benefits identified by the author are building personal connections, the ability to learn from others, and an increase in self-efficiency and perseverance in the face of adversity. These connections provide people with meaningful relationships with friends and family. They offer resources to adapt to adversities, engage in meaningful activities, and the motivation to endure and continue to learn. Service is the key to a positive attitude and a sense of purpose.

Other studies have also outlined the beneficial impact of volunteer work in resilience building and faith restoration—including accounts of volunteers in palliative care settings and home visiting programs for isolated parents. Volunteer work has led to improvement in depressive symptoms among residents in continuing care retirement communities, in emotional survival for the unemployed, and for survivors of terrorist bombings.

Perils of Service for Healers

While the authors have discussed the relevance of service as a crucial dimension of enduring recovery for addicts, excessive preoccupation with service may also be detrimental to recovery. There are "Wounded Healers" who become overly focused on service to others as a way of healing themselves. While this approach may be socially beneficial, recovering addicts run the risk of burnout in work and life. This may become detrimental not only to their own health but the health of loved ones and of society in general.

A seminal article on the subject summarized the findings of research in this matter as follows:

Physicians, especially those involved in direct patient care, were more likely than the average individual to have relatively poor marriages, to use drugs and alcohol heavily, and to obtain psychotherapy. Although these difficulties are often assumed to be occupational hazards of medicine, their presence or absence appeared to be strongly associated with life adjustment before medical school. Only the physicians with the least stable childhoods and adolescent adjustments appeared vulnerable to these occupational hazards. The finding may contribute to the medical and psychological management of physician patients.

Vulnerable healers project their inner orphan onto their patients. By taking care of the patient, they are subconsciously taking care of their own inner wounds and childhood emotional deprivations. When this becomes symptomatic in healers, they may fall prey to addiction, depression, marital strife, or medical problems. This dynamic must be addressed. The healer must attend to her/his self-care and life/work balance. This includes sectors of life such as love, creativity, play, and prayer.

Cultivation of Faith

The following methods would be good initial steps towards the cultivation of faith to support the transcendent function of addicts in recovery:

Spiritual Purposefulness
The Healing Impact of Having Purpose in Life
The Healing Impact of Volunteer Activities (Service)
The Dynamics of Hope
Prayer
Fellowship and Community
The Healing Wisdom of the Body
Fasting
Exercise
Good Sleep
The Power of Positivity (Fake it till you make it!)
Faith Restoration
Kenosis (Empty your cup)
Pranayama
Iyengar Yoga
Saint Ignatius' Month-long Retreat

Vipasana Practice
Meditation
Mindfulness
The Breakout Principle
(The Nitrous Oxide Phenomenon)
Living Your Personal Myth

Let us now explore these various methods.

Chapter 4

Dynamics of Hope

WHEN FACED WITH a crisis or catastrophe—whether addiction or cancer—the ego succumbs to despair and loss of hope. According to recent studies, the treatment of the disease may be impersonal, but the treatment of the patient must always be personal and invoke a sense of hope. Hope should be a practice. That is, hope at its core is "something you do" rather than "something you feel." A practice is a program of action undertaken, not for utilitarian reasons, but rather to shape one's being as a person and how one chooses to live in relation to oneself and others.

Research has repeatedly found hope to be a major determinant in effectively dealing with the distress and uncertainty of a cancer diagnosis. Hope may also have direct effects on physical health. The three general strategies for mobilizing hope include: (1) individual problem-solving, (2) relational coping, and (3) mobilizing your core identity. Assessing a patient's ability to handle past adversities can guide the selection of a hope-building strategy for coping better with present challenges.

Hope has been defined as the product of "pathways thinking" and "agency thinking." *Pathways thinking* begins by envisioning a desired future state, then imagining paths from one's current situation to that future state, and then formulating the steps proposed to be taken along those paths. *Agency thinking* is the self-talk that helps sustain a sense of personal agency (i.e., that one can act effectively). Pathways thinking combined with agency-thinking turns "lemons into lemonade," obstacles into stepping-stones, and traumas into challenges according to these studies.

Clinically, hope is best regarded not as a reactive feeling, but as a set of practices that can help people to keep moving steadily towards their desires and commitments, despite the adversities of illness and its treatment. By examining how a patient has responded to past adversities, a clinician can discern whether a patient's best hope-building competencies lie in problem-solving as an individual, in relational coping that relies on help from others, or in accessing emotional energy from a core identity.

Prayer

The most common form of self-healing is prayer, a gateway to the profound mystery of the sacred. Some writers propose that we may be wired for God, while others speculate that humans may have a "God gene." According to *Scientific American*, a researcher looked at the DNA samples of some of his subjects, hoping to find variants of genes that tended to turn up in self-transcendent people. His search led to a gene known as VMAT2. Two different versions of this gene exist, differing only at a single position. People with one version of the gene tend to score a little higher on self-transcendence tests. Although the influence is small, it is consistent. About half the people in the study had at least one copy of the self-transcendence boosting version of VMAT2, "the God gene."

Others propose that humanity's perception of a spiritual realm is actually the biological result of thousands of years of evolution. In other words, the God gene is "nature's white lie," a coping mechanism selected into our species to help alleviate the debilitating anxiety caused by our unique awareness of death.

Two academics at the University of Pennsylvania's Center for Spirituality and the Mind contend that contemplating God actually reduces stress, which in turn prevents the deterioration of the brain's dendrites, and increases neuroplasticity. They concluded that meditation and other spiritual practices permanently strengthen neural functioning in specific parts of the brain that aid in lowering anxiety and depression, thus enhancing social awareness, empathy, and improving cognitive functioning.

Of course, the role of religion, spirituality, community, and prayer in health has been a subject of debate for a long time. The Rosetta study investigated the striking differences in mortality from myocardial infarction between Rosetta, a homogeneous Italian-American community in Pennsylvania, and other nearby towns between 1955 and 1965. These differences disappeared as Rosetta became more "Americanized" in the 1960s. A more recent study extended the comparison over a longer period of time to test the hypothesis that the findings from this period were not due to random fluctuations in small communities. The researchers examined death certificates for Rosetta and Bangor, Maine from 1935 to 1985. Age-standardized death rates and mortality ratios were computed for each decade. They found that the Rosettans had a lower mortality rate from myocardial infarction over the course of the first thirty years, but that mortality rose to the level of Bangor's following a period of erosion of traditional cohesive family and community relationships. This mortality-rate increase involved mainly younger Rosetan men and elderly women. The data confirmed the existence of consistent mortality differences between Rosetta and Bangor during a time when there were many indicators of greater social solidarity and homogeneity in Rosetta.

The unanswered question in the Rosetta study was whether the differences in mortality rates in the two towns were related to community or religion. A further study emphasized that religious observance had a strong positive influence on protecting health. Researchers assessed the association of Jewish religious observance with mortality by comparing religious and secular kibbutzim. Such collectives are highly similar in social structure and economic function, and are cohesive and supportive communities. A sixteen-year (1970–1985) study of mortality in eleven religious and eleven secular kibbutzim found that mortality was considerably higher in secular kibbutzim. The lower mortality in religious kibbutzim was consistent for all major causes of death.

Another study found a positive therapeutic effect from intercessory prayer in coronary-care patients

(65). The therapeutic effects of prayer, one of the oldest forms of therapy, have received little attention in medical literature. To evaluate the effects in a coronary-care unit (CCU) population, a prospective randomized double-blind protocol was followed. Over ten months, 393 patients admitted to the CCU were randomized, after signing informed consent, to either an intercessory prayer group or to a control group. While hospitalized, the first group received intercessory prayer from participating Christians praying outside the hospital; the control group did not. At entry, analysis revealed no statistical difference between the groups. After entry, all patients were followed for the remainder of the admission. The prayer group subsequently had significantly better results; patients in the control group required ventilatory assistance, antibiotics, and diuretics more frequently. According to Randolph, this data suggests that intercessory prayer to the Judaeo-Christian God has a beneficial therapeutic effect in patients admitted to a CCU.

The Bible reveals many types of prayers and employs a variety of words to describe the practice. For example, 1 Timothy 2:1 says, "First of all I urge that supplications, prayers, intercessions, and thanksgiving be made for everyone." Here, all four of the main Greek words used for prayer are mentioned in one verse.

The following are the nine main types of prayers mentioned in the Bible:

The Prayer of Faith

James 5:15 says, "The prayer said in faith will save the sick person, and the Lord will raise him up." In this context, prayer is offered in faith for someone who is sick, asking God to heal. When we pray, we are to believe in the power and goodness of God (Mark 9:23).

The Prayer of Agreement

After Jesus' ascension, the disciples "all gave themselves to constant prayer with one mind" (Acts 1:14). Later, after Pentecost, the early church "devoted themselves" to prayer (Acts 2:42). Their example encourages us to pray with others.

The Prayer of Request (or Supplication)

We are to take our requests to God. Philippians 4:6 teaches, "Do not be anxious about anything. In everything resort to prayer and supplication together with thanksgiving and bring your requests before God." Part of winning the spiritual battle is to "pray at all times as the Spirit inspires you with all prayer and supplication" (Ephesians 6:18).

The Prayer of Thanksgiving

We see another type of prayer again in Philippians 4:6—thanksgiving or thanks to God. "With thanksgiving bring your requests before God." Many examples of thanksgiving prayers can be found in the Psalms.

The Prayer of Worship

The prayer of worship is similar to the prayer of thanksgiving. The difference is that worship focuses on who God is; thanksgiving focuses on what God has done. Church leaders in Antioch prayed in this manner with fasting: "While they were worshipping the Lord and fasting, the Holy Spirit said to them, 'Set apart for me Barnabas and Saul to do the work for which I have called them.' So after fasting and praying they laid their hands on them and sent them off" (Acts 13:2-3).

The Prayer of Consecration

Sometimes, prayer is a time of setting ourselves apart to follow God's will. Jesus made such a prayer the night before His crucifixion: "He went a little farther and fell to the ground with his face touching the earth, and prayed, 'Father, if it is possible, take this cup away from me. Yet not what I want, but what you want'" (Matthew 26:39).

The Prayer of Intercession

Our prayers often include requests for others. We are told to make intercession "for everyone" in 1 Timothy 2:1. Jesus serves as an example. The whole of John 17 is a prayer of Jesus on behalf of his disciples and all believers.

The Prayer of Imprecation

Imprecatory prayers are found in Psalms 7, 55, and 69. They are used to invoke God's judgment on the wicked and thereby avenge the righteous. The psalmists use this type of appeal to emphasize the holiness of God and the surety of His judgment. However, Jesus taught us to pray for our enemies (Matthew 5:44-48).

More on Prayer

The Bible also speaks of praying in the Spirit (1 Corinthians 14:14-15) and of offering prayers even when we are unable to think of adequate words (Romans 8:26-27). In those times, the Spirit Himself intercedes for us.

Prayer is conversation with God and should be made without ceasing (1 Thessalonians 5:16-18). As we grow in our love for Jesus Christ, we will naturally desire to talk to him.

The gist of this was well summarized by Carl Jung in his communication to AA co-founder Bill W. In a letter dated 23 January 1961, he traced the story of Rowland H., who, having exhausted all treatment efforts for his alcoholism, became Jung's patient for a year (1931) and showed much improvement. However, he soon relapsed and returned to Jung as a last resort. Jung confronted him with the hopelessness of his situation and the futility of any further treatment options—with the possible exception of a religious or spiritual experience.

Shortly thereafter, Rowland joined the Oxford Group, an evangelical movement in Europe that emphasized the principles of self-survey, confession, restitution, and service to others. After his conversion experience released him from alcoholism, Rowland returned to New York and helped Edwin T. (Ebby) to achieve sobriety. Ebby inspired Bill W. to seek his own recovery by acknowledging the collapse of his ego followed by a spiritual experience. Ebby gave Bill W., a copy of William James' *Varieties of Religious Experience*, which explores this conversion process. With the guidance of his physician, Dr. William Silkworth, Bill W. went on to establish Alcoholics Anonymous.

In his response to Bill W. on 30 January 1961, Jung identified an alcoholic or addict's craving as a low-level equivalent of our spiritual thirst for wholeness—a union with God. As we've seen earlier, alcohol in Latin is called *spiritus*. Thus the same word is used for the highest religious experience and a potentially depraving poison. The helpful formula therefore is: *Spiritus contra Spiritum.*

Our relationship tangles with friends and foe alike, our dreams and creative processes are manifestations of a yearning for connection with this spiritus. The path from illness to wellness is a search for the Spirit.

Fellowship and Community

Fellowship is another important aspect of the recovery process. If we attempt to get sober on our own, we are missing out on the most significant dimension of support and guidance from the fellowship that may bolster our effort towards sobriety. Recent neuroscience findings corroborate the timeless wisdom that we need the *Sangha* (Buddhist word for fellowship) to gain spiritual awareness.

In his communication with Bill W., Jung asserted that for an addict to recover, he needs to establish spiritual engagement and community:

> I am strongly convinced that the evil principle prevailing in this world leads to unrecognized spiritual need into perdition if it is not counteracted either by religious insight or by the protective wall of human community.
>
> *—Carl Jung's Letter to Bill W.*
> *(30 January 1961)*

The crucial dimension of community is well established in many religious traditions. A sense of belonging is essential for consolidating one's spiritual awakening.

This is well established in the 12-Step Program and can be found in the value people find in other institutions such as professional societies or fraternal lodges. Neuroscience research indicates that it may be crucial for our society to establish a sense of community for its members in childhood: in schools and in families; through group activities for children; and in other initiatives to create a supportive and nurturing community to counter the scourge of addiction and other psychiatric turbulences. Such bonding in community will enhance the lifelong resilience of individuals.

There is emerging neuroscientific evidence that community and social networks improve the functioning of the connective white matter of our brain, insulated by a substance called myelin. A recent article in the *Journal of the American Medical Association* summarizes the dynamic regulation of the myelination process in health and disease. Previous neurology models considered the myelination process to be something static. However, recent human imaging studies have revealed changes in myelin that correlate with various types of experience. One study shows how piano training exhibits white matter alterations in brain regions involved in sensitive motor processing that correlate with years of practice.

Other studies reveal the role of social experience on myelin development and function in the prefrontal cortex of the brain, which has been implicated in multiple psychiatric disorders. Mice subjected to social isolation experience prefrontal cortex hypo myelination and display cognitive and social impairments. Projecting this finding onto human relationships implies that lack of a supportive social milieu can lead to prefrontal cortex dysfunction, impairing our faculty for self-awareness and self-regulation.

Researchers propose that myelin plasticity may contribute to psychiatric illness in a number of ways. Experiences that result in thinner myelin could hinder neuronal communication, leading to cognitive impairments as seen in several psychiatric and, perhaps, addictive disorders.

However not all socialization leads to a positive outcome. It is possible that certain regions of myelination in other brain regions may reinforce neural pathways involved in maladaptive, cognitive, emotional, or behavioral patterns. We may see this play out in the negative outcomes associated with maladaptive groups, such as criminally-minded gangs.

Carl Jung's Story of Faith Restoration

Following his breakup with Freud and personal and professional isolation in neutral Switzerland during World War I, Jung was depressed and encountered his dark night of the soul. He lost faith in himself, his mentor, the world, and the future. The story of his faith restoration and resilience is instructive. As a spiritual mentor of AA and the 12-Step Program, his thoughts are also of value to anyone concerned with the treatment of addiction.

> After the parting of ways with Freud, a period of inner uncertainty began for me. It would be no exaggeration to call it a state of disorientation. I felt totally suspended in mid-air for I had not yet found my footing …
>
> On 1 August, World War I broke out. Now my task was clear; I had to understand what had happened and to what extent my own experience coincided with that of humankind in general. Therefore my first obligation was to probe the depths of my own psyche. I made a beginning by writing down my fantasies which came to me during my

building game. This work took precedence over everything else.

The Transcendent Function

In a 1916 essay on the transcendent function of the mind, Jung lays out the instructions for deploying active imagination in treating addiction and other maladies. Active imagination offers a template to bridge the conscious with the unconscious, the ego with the soul, and the personal with the collective. It opens up a wellspring of guidance from the symbols of the psyche that can guide our adaptation to crisis, developmental challenges, trauma, and growth opportunities. It can become the invitation to claim our teleos or destiny. Once we assimilate the guidance of the soul via the transcendent function, we establish a new baseline of our personality until new challenges and opportunities call for a fresh adaptation. For healthy individuals, individuation is an unending process, guided by the GPS of symbols from our souls. It becomes the perpetual source of resilience for the vicissitudes of the human condition.

We can access and assimilate the guidance of our souls through the archetypes or timeless wisdom embedded in our psyches and located in our limbic nervous systems. They are the ancestral memory of human civilization encoded in our DNA. They give us guidance during times of transition and change, crisis and trauma, development, and initiation.

From Ego Resilience to Soul Emergence

Now that we have explored the available research on resilience from a conventional psychological, psychiatric, and neuroscientific perspective, let us beg to disagree with conventional psychiatry and amplify a few key parameters of the existing paradigms. While available research emphasizes adaptation, Jungian psychology and many Eastern religious traditions call for going beyond ego adaptation to nothing less than soul-guided individuation and a transformation of personality. According to Jung's *Red Book*, a crisis or trauma can provide the sand grit around which the oyster of our personality may incubate the pearl of individuation and emergence. The breakdown of the ego is an opportunity for the breakthrough of the soul.

Chapter 5

From Adaptation to Transformation

OUR BIASED WAY of thinking often has us consider that instinct is bad and the spirit is good. Jung made a significant observation: instinct and spirit are both good and bad. Whenever an individual is stuck at one end of the spectrum of instinct or spirit, he becomes emotionally lopsided and imbalanced in his thinking, devoid of a center point of reference. A person who runs his life on instinct, devoid of spiritual inclinations, risks becoming an animal, a souless creature. A person who is all spirit—and lacks the instinct to engage his spiritual insight—can become nothing more than a hot air balloon with no ground to stand on. Such an individual is pure rhetoric and no substance. Thus, instinct or spirit acting in isolation makes for an unhealthy atmosphere.

Instinct *informed* by the spirit, with the spirit *supported* by the instinct, is good. This is what Jung describes as a *Complexio Oppositorum* or union of opposites in the psyche.

So how does one establish this *Complexio Oppositorum*? Jung insisted that we must engage our *feeling function.* Whenever we reach a crossroads or undertake a new enterprise in life, we must ask ourselves: What is of value? What feels right? What feels soulful and purposeful? This may call for considerable reflection. At times even the most focused deliberation may not yield the answer. At this point, one must go beyond the boundary of individual consciousness for guidance from the soul and the Universe. This will yield the necessary insight, images, and symbols needed to guide one's path in uniting the opposites in a manner that honors our life purpose and personal narrative.

Buddhists Call This the Third Way

The safest place when fording a river is on either side— but standing safely on the riverside gets us nowhere. The most turbulent spot in the river is in the middle. Buddhists call this the third possibility. Wading into the river we risk being swept away, but by doing so we are most likely to reach our destination—the ocean, the spiritual source and destination of all existence. Most of Jung's work and clinical methods act as a guide to engaging this flow and finding our own center of value and purpose in life. Specifically, he evolved the clinical method of active imagination—the middle way between the ego and the soul—to find one's spiritual destiny, the *teleos*. In daily life, we must always struggle to stay in our body and act on our instincts, while simultaneously staying reflective about the guidance of the soul to help us navigate the middle way. Christ did not just have lofty spiritual ideas. He actually put his life on the line and surmounted it by way of sacrificing his body on the Cross to fulfil his spiritual destiny as the Savior. The Holy Spirit guided him on the value of his life and purpose. At the end he chose spiritual purpose over the instinct of survival.

Thus, our life is a constant dance between instinct and spirit, each pulling in opposite directions. It is a struggle between the animal (reptilian) brain and the reasoning (neocortical) brain. When these opposites pull, the limbic (emotional) brain and its archetypes offer an image. A symbol to unite these opposites is the ouroboros or tail-eating serpent. The ouroboros is a connecting symbol for our triune brain and a manifestation of our wholeness. The center of the ouroboros is our soul, which creates an energy field that organizes our instincts and spiritual purpose into a meaningful circle or mandala of enterprise. Our life now does not meander like a snake on the prowl for its victim, but rather engages its instinctual tail in a spiritual, reflective, value-guided trajectory of life.

The ouroboros thus embodies the space, the gap, the flow between instinct and spirit, body and soul, matter and psyche. What connects these dots is the fourth dimension of consciousness, what Jung termed the psychoid space. This dimension is invisible, but fortunately we have archetypes that are accessible to our consciousness as images, ideas, and symbols. Their infinite and countless variations are unique to each individual and situation in which they are activated. Matter and psyche are two manifestations of the same energy. Quantum physics has bridged the arbitrary distinction between matter and psyche. In scientific experiments, an atom may manifest as matter or energy—depending upon how the observer sets up the experiment. In Jung's analytical psychology, we see further evidence of this unity in the phenomena of synchronicity and transcendent function.

In his masterpiece *Mysterium Coniunctionis*, Jung summarizes a lifetime of wisdom on the individuation process and the union of opposites in the psyche. Our psyche exists on a continuum of *Unio Naturalis* (in continuum with nature—both our own nature and nature around us); *Unio Mentalis* (the psychological lens with which we look at ourselves, at others, at the world and the future); *Unio Spiritualis* (a manifestation of our spiritual purpose); *Unio Corporalis* (the soul manifesting in the body); and *Unus Mundus* (the individual soul connected with the world soul or primal spirit, the union of *Atman* with *Brahman*). Jung was trying to establish the interconnection between these different manifestations of the soul in nature, mentation, cognition, spirituality, body, and the world.

Jung's concept has significant clinical and practical implications for understanding and healing human suffering, including addiction. For example, if there is an unresolved emotional or relationship issue—a *heart chakra* problem as defined in Hindu tradition—and it is not attended to, that relationship issue may manifest itself as a heart problem. In other words, a relationship or emotional problem of *Unio Mentalis* may manifest as a cardiac problem in the realm of *Unio Corporalis*. Similarly, if an individual has an unmodulated sexual drive, it may manifest as prostate cancer. Here a natural instinctual drive, when unbridled, manifests as a cancer. This is where *Unio Naturalis* in the instinctual realm, if unattended, may manifest in the body realm of *Unio Corporalis*.

The gem of this hypothesis lies in the treatment implications. If the problem in one realm could be traced to its origins, it could be reconfigured and the psyche could be reset to a more adaptive mode. The idea of Quantum physics is extremely applicable at this point. By activating the healing zone of consciousness, we enter the transcendent realm. Here the states of *Unio Naturalis, Mentalis, Spiritualis, Corporalis,* and *Unus Mundus* re-establish a fluid, interchangeable continuum that may then be reset to a more optimal level of physical, mental and spiritual functioning. Otherwise a core problem in one of these realms may manifest itself as a medical, psychiatric, relationship, or spiritual problem. While Jung had access to the emerging theories of Quantum physics and the interchangeability of matter and energy, wave and particle, he did not have the time to evolve his theories to their practical and clinical boundaries, that task falling to the modern practitioners of mind-body medicine.

An example: if a face looks distorted on the computer screen, one can go to the original binary program and by correcting the code in the original computer file, one can reset the image on the screen. A sceptic can say that it is one thing to correct the facial image on the computer screen, but can we reset the facial problem in real life using this method? Our response is that in some instances we can. If the facial distortion is related to a genetic disorder, we may be getting close to a day when genomic reset in one's DNA pattern may actually help reconfigure many parts, organs and functions of the body and the mind. These genomic and quantum pieces of the jig-saw puzzle were the two missing pieces which precluded Jung from pursuing his masterpiece *Mysterium Coniunctionis* to its fullest potential of therapeutic implications.

Neuroscience focuses on resilience training as an important dimension of trauma management as well as ego consolidation, which is crucial for management of the symptoms and adaptation. However, analytical psychology also attends to the transformative value of trauma, guided by the *trimurti* archetype in Hindu mythology represented by Shiva, the destroyer, with the help of *Shakti*; Brahma, the creator in consort with goddess Saraswati; and Vishnu, the preserver, in collaboration with Laxmi. This trinitarian archetype presides over the eternal cycle of destruction, creation and consolidation, imparting resilience to individuals and cultures in the face of trauma and constant change.

In Greek mythology, the archetype of the phoenix is a useful symbol of resilience in the face of trauma.

Associated with the sun, the phoenix is a creature who obtains new life by arising from the ashes of its predecessor. The phoenix was subsequently adopted as a symbol in early Christianity of Christ's resurrection.

When we deal with adversity in life, our resilience stems from our soul and its continuity with the spirit—the yoking of the *Atman* with the *Brahman*. Analytical psychology offers a method—the transcendent function to access this mystery via our personal symbols and the timeless wisdom of the archetypes encoded in the psyche of every person, culture, and the collective.

During the process of individuation, as well as in times of crisis, trauma, initiations, and developmental transitions, our true self makes itself known through the transcendent function. It can manifest itself as an image, hunch, dream, synchronistic event, accident, complex, relationship tangle, medical or psychiatric symptom, fascination with a painting or a movie, or an interest in a fairy tale. These all offer clues that can guide us onto our path to individuation and resilience. The hope is that we will find what we are meant to be, our *Dharma*, as the Hindus say.

Chapter 6

The Healing Wisdom of the Body

ADDICTS REGRESS TO the spirits found in the bottle to engage their spiritual craving, literally in the case of alcoholism and metaphorically when abusing other drugs, food, sex, the internet, gambling, pornography, or codependency. Such behavior establishes negative and maladaptive "neurosignatures" or brain circuits to deal with these cravings. Dr. Herbert Benson discusses this concept in his groundbreaking book, *Timeless Healing*. Other researchers have outlined the importance of the concept of "Interoception," the physiological condition of the body as an information channel, crucial in our self-awareness, and vulnerable to perceived stress and threats to our well-being.

The emotional processing center in the limbic brain is the amygdala. The sensation of threat activates the amygdala, which then consults the medial prefrontal cortex for a quick check on how our body is feeling. If this Interoception indicates that the body is calm, it reassures the amygdala, aborting the primal stress or trauma response of fight, flight or freeze. The therapeutic implication is that stabilizing our Interoception through a contemplative method like yoga, meditation, or mindfulness will result in a calming impact on the amygdala.

The key question in moving from addiction to sobriety and spirituality remains: how do we engage the Spirit rather than resort to the bottle or other forms of addiction? How do we restore positive neurosignatures and healthy Interoception? The Kripa Foundation's Model of Recovery with emphasis on yoga is one way to attend to this problem.

Cultivating Resilience and Restoring Faith in Recovering Addicts

Cultivation of psychological resilience is a crucial aspect of the faith restoration that must occur during recovery from an addiction. While resilience is defined as the capacity of an individual to rebound to their baseline level of functioning, it is our clinical experience that when dealing with stress, crisis, or trauma, the outcome is not simply resilience—but either an enduring impairment or substantial improvement in baseline functioning. As Nietzsche famously said,

"If it does not kill you, it may make you stronger." The goal of resilience training is to make us stronger.

Resilience is a dynamic process encompassing positive adaptation within the context of adversity. Implicit within this notion are two critical conditions: exposure to significant threats or severe adversity; and the achievement of positive adaptation despite major assaults on the developmental process. Three factors are involved in the development of resilience in individuals: their personal attributes, their families, and their wider social environments. As research evolved, it became clear that positive adaptation—despite exposure to adversity—involves a developmental progression; new vulnerabilities and strengths often emerge with changing life circumstances.

The study of resilience as a process of development has overturned many negative assumptions about children growing up under the threat of disadvantage and adversity. The most surprising conclusion that emerges from studies of these children is the ordinariness of resilience. Recent findings suggest that resilience is common and usually arises from the normative functions of human adaptation systems, with the greatest threats to human development being those that compromise these protective systems. The conclusion that resilience is made of ordinary rather than extraordinary personality traits offers a more positive outlook on human development and adaptation, as well as a direction for policies and practices to enhance the development of at-risk children. There is less reason, based on this research, for loss of hope.

Chapter 7

Neuroscience of Resilience

RECENT EVIDENCE FROM animal research underscores the extraordinary plasticity of the brain and demonstrates that early social experience, in particular, has profound consequences for the developing nervous system. The possibilities of transforming this circuitry in adulthood, with specific methods designed to cultivate a positive effect, are heartening.

Plastic changes in the brain can be produced by various methods, including meditation. The Dalai Lama raised this point in his book *The Art of Happiness*. He explains that the very structure and function of the brain allows for the systematic training of the mind with the goal of cultivating happiness, a genuine inner transformation that can be achieved by deliberately selecting and focusing on positive mental states and challenging negative mental states. The wiring in our brains is not static, not irrevocably fixed. Our brains are remarkably adaptable.

Trauma Research

Emerging neuroscience research has examined this from many perspectives, particularly in trauma research. A recent study found that different neural patterns distinguish resilient veterans from those with PTSD, and suggests an important role in the healthy response to trauma. Science has located a site for resilience in the nervous system. The right superior temporal gyrus may be one of the neural pathways for the ego/self-axis and the transcendent function. Stress and trauma research have made substantial contributions to our understanding of the neuroscience behind our resilience in adaptively coping and mastering these challenges. In his recent book on trauma, Bessel Van der Kolk has synthesized these findings and their implications in a masterful way. Here is a brief summary of some recent findings.

For an optimal response to stress and trauma, a balance must be maintained between our reptilian (or survival) brain, our limbic (or emotional) brain, and our neocortical (or rational) brain. If we get caught in the reptilian brain, we succumb to the fight, fright, or freeze responses with the accompanying psychological, physiological, immunological, and clinical manifestations of anxiety and stress. These include activation of high levels of epinephrine and steroid levels in blood and brain, acidic inner environment, weakening of the immune system, and abnormalities in blood pressure, pulse, and heart rate.

When an addict is in the throes of addiction, his primary reaction to the stress of daily life is the reptilian response. Fortunately, we can move our reptilian nervous system from stress to relaxation and recuperation by activating the parasympathetic nervous system through regulating our breath, a practice called *pranayama* in the Hindu tradition. This calms and soothes our system, lowers pulse rate and blood pressure, increases the acetyl choline and oxytocin levels in our body, creates a restorative alkaline inner environment, improves our mood, and strengthens our immune system. To be in the relaxation and recuperation mode is the goal of faith restoration, resilience training and an active recovery program.

If we get caught in the emotional-limbic brain, we lose touch with the rational-neocortical brain. When stress or crisis activates our emotional-limbic brain beyond the threshold of our comfort zone of adaptation, it triggers a reptilian response, blocking the rational-neocortical response of measured, voluntary willpower-based choice. We lapse into survival mode rather than rational or mastery mode. This is the primary process of response in addiction disorders. The reason behind this detour is the neural circuitry of our brain.

Resonance Circuits

The process of Interoception, mentioned earlier, is greatly impacted by the presence of another person and his/her relationship to us. Sometimes, it is not the other person himself, but who he reminds us of. Additionally, our mirror neurons are tuned into the unconscious intent of the other person not just his conscious behavior. In other words, our neurons can be activated by what the other intends to do, not what they are doing. Jung addressed the phenomenon in his discussion of the unconscious-to-unconscious connection between two individuals, which is the basis of the clinical phenomenon of projective identification (8).

This Interoceptive response to the other is mediated in part by what UCLA clinical psychiatrist Daniel Siegel refers to as the "Resonance Circuit." This resonance to other people induces the Interoceptive response, mediated by the insula in the limbic system, which is activated via the mirror neurons (100). The insula sends neural signals to the brain stem, the autonomic nervous system and the body, and it replicates the "self-state" of the other person in our body. This then activates the amygdala, which further consults the ventral-medial prefrontal cortex for verification of the Interoception before activating the stress or relaxation response.

The phenomenon of resonance circuits has significant implications in understanding the dynamics of resilience to deal with addictions. Old timers in the 12-Step Program share a piece of wisdom: "Stick with the winners!" If we stick with the winners, we are infused with their sense of integrity, hope and purposefulness. If we surround ourselves with losers, we resonate with their negativity and despair, and will likely go down with their personal Titanics. This also has implications for vulnerable children absorbing the negative Interoceptive self-states of their parents. This phenomenon is well documented in the adult children of alcoholics and plays out similarly in all dysfunctional families. One study examined the birth order in the adult children of alcoholics. The eldest son is often the family hero, a rescuer of the dysfunctional system. The second or the middle child is the scapegoat, who takes the rap to protect other vulnerable members of the family from the abusive parent. In other scenarios, the middle child takes on the role of the lost child who does not wish to add to the burdens of an overtaxed system. The youngest child is often the family mascot, who provides comic relief in a distressed system.

The resonance phenomenon has therapeutic implications for therapist-patient relationships. Both parties may resonate from contact with each other's self-states. The therapist is expected to make use of this resonance of empathy, insight, support and interpretation. A sensitive therapist can feel the self-state of a patient, replicating their angst in his body and mind. If the therapist can digest or transmute his self-state in his psyche through contemplative methods—such as *pranayama*, meditation or mindfulness—he can transfer a relaxed self-state to his patient. Healers in India have used these methods for several thousand years in the pranic breathing techniques. The healer notes the turbulence in his breath in response to the patient and then steadies his own breath. This can have a salutary effect on calming even the most agitated patients.

CASE STUDY:

A therapist met a patient in analysis every Thursday at 3 pm after his tea break. On other days at 3 pm, he felt relaxed after tea. He felt fine Thursdays at 2 and 4 pm but at 3 pm would invariably get an upper backache. He was intrigued by this pattern. Finally it dawned on him that it had something to do with the Thursday patient. Discussing this with her, he observed that she had had suffered from chronic upper back pain since her teen years (she was in her sixties now). The therapist discovered that he had an empathic resonance with her Interoceptive self-state of the upper back pain. The patient was the oldest child of an alcoholic father and a depressed mother, and had been the emotional caretaker of her younger siblings all her life. She had a caretaker complex and was living out the archetype of Atlas, the mythical hero who carries the burden of the earth on his back for perpetuity. Analytically, she was able to work through her caretaker complex and gradually move from co-dependency to compassionate detachment and gradually attend to her own growth and aspirations.

The resonance circuit can manifest even in a dream state. Jenny, a patient who is a forty-something mother, reported a dream in her psychotherapy session.

> I am in bed playing with my four-year-old daughter. My mood is playful. Suddenly I playfully start to tickle my daughter and the little girl laughs.
>
> This dream awakened Jenny, who then heard her daughter in her room down the hallway. She went to check and found that the little girl was fast asleep but laughing and mumbling, "Mom, don't tickle me." The mother-daughter pair had established a resonance circuit in their sleep.

Uncoupling Negative Bluetooth Resonance

Another useful concept, particularly in relationship problems and distressed marriages, is the phenomenon of "Interoceptive autonomy." When one partner is stressed he may tend to project this onto the other, albeit unconsciously. In other words, the partner with a higher degree of emotional valiancy can "Bluetooth" this inner state onto his or her partner. The goal of Interoceptive autonomy is to uncouple this unconscious Bluetooth phenomenon.

Case Study:

A woman was extremely unhappy in her job for which she was overqualified. At home she was chronically angry and critical of her husband. He described her attitude as shooting bullets the minute she was home from work. The husband tried to appease, capitulate, placate, and please her—all unsuccessfully. He would get into an anxious, agitated state when all his efforts to restore peace proved unfruitful. He tried to explain himself, or take evasive and corrective measures, e.g., clean the house several times before she came home. Yet he often bought into her projections that he was a sloppy person. At this point, he had established a Bluetooth connection with her distressed inner state.

At one point, the therapist invited him to monitor his self-state, breath, heart rate, and muscle tension. He found that these went off balance the minute she got home. The therapist recommended that he practice intentional breath management or *pranayama*, and maintain the autonomy of his self-state or Interoception when he felt this imbalance with her. Although he was careful to not offend her, he stopped making extraordinary efforts to placate her. He imagined that the bullets flying towards him were just an illusion and would melt away before they pierced him. He started to uncouple from this negative Bluetooth personal area network in which he was caught.

Once he started practicing Interoceptive autonomy, his wife started to feel more and more agitated, but he refused to buy into her projections. After a short time something interesting happened. His wife broke down and started to cry, acknowledged that she was unhappy and undervalued at work, and actually had a tantrum in her workplace instead of home. A few weeks later, after a high level meeting with her management, she was promoted to a position with pay commensurate with her credentials and training. She became much happier as did her spouse.

When we start to recognize that we are in a Bluetooth coupling mode, resonating with the turbulent mental state of the others around us, we must go to a place of empathy but detachment, what the Buddhists call compassionate detachment. By maintaining our Interoceptive autonomy, we can break the vicious

Bluetooth cycle of negative resonance, and free both parties to claim their own corrective path. This leads to relational resilience and creates a win-win situation. When this is not possible, one must withdraw from a negative relationship since it is soul abuse to subject oneself to it. It confirms the adage, "Stick with the Winners!"

Resonance and the Collective Unconscious

While neuroscience has made considerable strides in recent years towards understanding resonance circuits, mirror neurons, and the resonance field of empathy between individuals, Carl Jung was many years ahead of the curve. He postulated that individuals, tuned into the flow of the consciousness of the Universe, have the potential to establish resonance with the collective wisdom and the memory of our shared human consciousness through what he called the "collective unconscious." When we tune into this flow of deeper consciousness, we can access it to guide us. Later in his writings, Jung moved away from calling this flow the collective unconscious and termed it the "objective psyche," the profound substrate of our collective and deeper consciousness.

Regardless of the terminology, we can log in to this realm via our dreams, contemplative practices like *pranayama*, yoga, meditation, mindfulness, and active imagination.

A suitably trained analyst will mediate his patient's transcendent function by helping him to bring the conscious and the unconscious together, with the goal of arriving at a new attitude. A patient in depression would like to know "what it is all for" and how to gain relief. In the intensity of the emotional disturbance itself lies the energy he should have at his disposal to remedy his troubled state of mind. Nothing is achieved by repressing the emotional disturbance. It is only when the conscious mind confronts the products of the unconscious that a positive reaction will ensue. There appear to be two main tendencies in this process.

One is the way of creative formulation, the other is the way of understanding. Consciousness is continually widened through the confrontation or integration with previously unconscious contents. Even if the addict has sufficient intelligence to understand the procedure, he may still lack the courage and self-confidence, or be too lazy, mentally or morally, or too cowardly, to make an effort. But where the necessary premises exist, the transcendent function not only forms a valuable addition to psychotherapeutic treatment, but gives the patient the inestimable advantage of assisting the analyst with his own resources, and of breaking a dependence which is often humiliating. It is a way of attaining liberation through one's own efforts and of finding the courage to be oneself.

An individual who establishes resonance with the objective psyche (or collective unconscious) gains access to the timeless wisdom and memory of human civilization. This expands our consciousness to deal with change, crisis, trauma, development, and initiation into new modes of being, doing and living at a much higher threshold. Such an individual is part of the world soul or *Unus Mundus*. Artists and creative individuals are tuned into or are resonant with the flow, and bring back to the rest of us sketches of our future, our *teleos*. The Great Russian artist Kandinsky, in an essay published at the dusk of his life, wrote, "Ask yourselves whether the work of art carried you away to a world unknown to you before. If so, what more do you want?" Kandinsky was speaking of the Transcendent Function of Art. And when we dream, or are mindful of our medical or psychiatric symptoms, our neuroses, complexes, relationship tangles, accidents, and synchronicities, we can find transcendent guidance if we are open to the whispers of our soul. These experiences can enrich our consciousness. We can become "in-formed," with a new consciousness formatted by our inner, timeless wisdom.

Creative individuals have found a way to dip into the timeless flow of the collective unconscious via contemplative practices. In an excellent article posted on *Huffington Post*, Carolyn Gregoire reviewed how some movers and shakers of our time were able to tap into the objective psyche. His biographers have shown how Apple co-founder Steve Jobs was inspired by his practice of Zen Buddhism to empathically tune into the wish of the masses for the simple, elegant lines of his Apple products. The Beatles worked through their creative malaise under the auspices of their then Guru Maharishi Mahesh Yogi and Transcendental Meditation. After returning from his ashram at Rishikesh in India, they composed the White Album. Whole Foods CEO John Mackey's meditation practice set the foundation for the healthy values that define his chain of food stores. Mackey shared in his book, *Conscious Capitalism*, that meditating helped him to realize his business' highest purpose. "My search for meaning and purpose led me into the counterculture movement of the late 1960s and 1970s," Mackey wrote. "I studied

Eastern philosophy and religion at the time and still practice both yoga and meditation. I studied ecology. I became a vegetarian."

Other creative individuals have tapped into the objective psyche via their dreams. In his book, *Mendeleyev's Dream: The Quest for the Elements*, author Paul Strathern recounts the night of 17 February 1869, when the Russian scientist Dmitri Mendeleyev went to bed frustrated by a puzzle he had been struggling with for years: how the atomic weights of the chemical elements could be grouped in some meaningful way—and one that, with any luck, would open a window onto the hidden structure of nature. He dreamed, as he later recalled, of "a table where all the elements fell into place as required." His intuition that when the elements were listed in order of weight, their properties repeated in regular intervals, gave rise to the Periodic Table of the Elements—which, though much revised since, underlies modern chemistry.

When an idea is incubating in the collective unconscious, it often emerges simultaneously through several individuals who are working on it from different perspectives at divergent places. Consider the discovery of the light bulb. British inventor Joseph Wilson Swan started experimenting with light bulb designs in 1850.

Thomas Edison and Swan filed the patents for the light bulb almost on the same day. Swan sued Edison for patent infringement and won. However, the two formed a company General Electric and became partners.

The phenomenon of Interoception is vital for modulating stress response and fostering the resilience of our psyches. When we accurately and adaptively center our self-state via the recalibration of our self-awareness, we can transform stress and trauma into survival and mastery. This is the method used for thousands of years in Indian healing paradigms including *pranayama*, yoga, meditation, mindfulness, music (*Gandharva* music therapy), touch (*Marma* therapy), smells (*aromatherapy*), and healing sound (*mantra*). The ancient set of ideas that comprise of Indian Ayurveda includes an elegant system for balancing our nature (*Dosha* balancing) and restoring the optimal balance of mind, body, and soul.

Interoception offers a crucial paradigm or regulation of our self-state in response to crisis, stress and trauma. If we are tuned into the self-state of another person, we can replicate their stress states or claim our own agency in self-regulation. This is the basis of the contemplative practices of the East. Such practices grant us a sense of mastery over our self-state, giving us considerable immunity from anxiety, and a powerful stress inoculation system.

The regulation of Interoception is also a significant self-soothing method. Via the Insula-Mirror Neurons network, it offers a framework to soothe and calm the patient by regulating his self-state, using centering techniques in therapy sessions. This is the basis of pranic healing. A therapist experiencing the anxious self-state of his patient can focus on regulating his own breath and center himself by using *pranayama*, as mentioned earlier. Once the therapist is centered, more often than not the anxious patient starts to relax and tunes into the therapist's self-state. Other methods of Interoceptive recalibration—such as mindfulness, meditation and use of mantras—have a similar effect. Besides being tools in the bag of an experienced therapist, they also provide a useful method for couples in distress, and for law enforcement personnel dealing with crisis situations and other stressful encounters.

Cultivation of Resilience and Recovery

The emerging frontiers of medical research feature findings that have some bearing on enhancing our resilience, which an individual may implement after clearing it with her personal physician. This is not meant to be an exhaustive meta-analysis but rather some common sense interventions that may be worth considering in your personal program of resilience boosters and general well-being.

Fasting—*Vrata*

Fasting is part of most spiritual, religious and contemplative traditions. It is embedded in the traditions of Hindus, of Muslims during Ramadan, Jews at Yom Kippur, and Roman Catholics and Eastern Orthodox during Lent. Many Hindus still regularly fast on Mondays to honor Lord Shiva and on Thursdays to honor the goddess Annapurna. There are many fasting rituals in India for special occasions and spiritual preparations to cleanse the mind, body and soul—a sort of kenosis to prepare the vessel of the body, a sacramental ritual to receive the gifts of the divine.

In the context of Hindu mythology, *vrata* denotes a religious practice to carry out certain obligations with a view to achieving divine blessing for the fulfilment of one or several desires. Etymologically, *vrata* is a Sanskrit word that means "to vow" or "to promise." A *vrata* may consist of one or more of several actions. Such actions may include complete or partial fasting on certain specific days; a pilgrimage to a particular place or places; the performance of certain rituals; and the recitation of mantras and prayers.

According to Hindu scriptures, *vrata* assists the practitioner in achieving and fulfilling his goals through divine grace and blessing. Sometimes, close relatives, or the family priest (*purohit*), may be entrusted with the obligation of performing the *vrata*. The object of performing *vrata* is as varied as human desire, and may include gaining back lost health and wealth, begetting offspring, or beseeching divine help during a difficult period in one's life.

In his thought-provoking book *Grain Brain*, Dr. David Perlmutter reviews many exciting findings that support the efficacy of ancient practices such as fasting as well as exercise to boost health and resilience. During fasting, the human body diverts its metabolism from deriving glucose from the liver and the muscles to a ketogenic pathway, whereby the liver now uses body fat to create ketones. These ketones are considered super-fuel for the brain, with positive implications for people suffering from Alzheimer's and Parkinson's.

Exercise

Exercise is good for the body as well as for the brain. It is a powerful epigenetic modulator that activates our longevity genes, and the genes for the brain's growth hormone. Exercise reverses memory decline in the elderly and enhances the growth of new brain cells in the hippocampus, the memory center. There is emerging evidence of a high correlation between physical and mental health.

Sound Sleep

The connection between optimal sleep and brain health is a hormone called leptin. In adult men, optimal sleep (usually seven to eight hours a night) leads to an increase in leptin levels, while poor sleep results in a plunge. Leptin is found in fat cells and impacts our inflammatory response and the autonomic nervous system. It increases the sympathetic system versus the parasympathetic. A high carbohydrate diet causes an initial increase in leptin levels, just as it does to insulin, but eventually the cells become leptin resistant. While leptin decreases our appetite and improves the inflammatory response system, its opposite is the hormone ghrelin, which is secreted by the stomach when we are hungry and builds up our appetite.

Insomnia causes an increase in the ghrelin levels, boosting appetite, carbohydrate cravings, and obesity, while reducing leptin levels and our autonomic preparedness to deal with stress. Thus, optimal sleep is essential for enhancing stress response and resilience.

Fake It till You Make It!

Neuroscientific studies on facial expressions suggest that muscular manipulations that result in positive facial expressions may lead to positive emotional states. Contracting the muscles involved in facial expressions by way of smiling or frowning can make emotions more intense, even when we are unaware that our expression has changed. Individuals given to intense frowning are commonly perceived as expressing negative emotions. Anger, fear, and sadness are associated with activity in the corrugator muscles under the eyes.

In one study, facial expressions were modified by using the botulinum toxin injection. The researchers concerned sought to study how faces were perceived by others after the denervation of frown muscles with injections for treatment of frown lines. Facial photographs were taken of volunteers before and after the botulinum toxin injections. These photographs were shown to viewers who were unaware of the procedure and asked to rate the expressed intensity of anger, sadness, fear, and happiness. According to their ratings faces with denervated frown muscle activity expressed relatively less anger (–40%), fear (–49%), sadness (–10%), and more happiness (+71%). The conclusion was succinct: Facial muscle activity is essential for both negative and positive emotional expression.

Mood affects a person's psyche. Successful participants in AA's 12-Step Program have often described the necessity of maintaining a positive mood: "Fake it till you make it!" The idea is indicative of the standard practice in most professional treatment facilities of attending to patients promptly, providing them with clean, light-colored clothing, paying attention to their daily activities, and most importantly, encouraging the staff to smile and to be generous in their use of humor.

"Fake it till you make it!" ties in well with Jung's concept of the "persona." He used the term to describe how one appears to oneself and the world, but not what one is. From the Hindu tradition comes the idea of the "wise old man (the *rishi*) who dwells in the heart." In every heart there dwells a sage or *rishi*. The problem is that we often do not believe it and so bury the wisdom within. Thus when we reconfigure the persona via therapeutic intervention, we are helping the patient step out of her temporary state of despair over addiction or other troubles, and into a sense of transcendence. Jung added that the persona is a mask we adopt. It comes into existence for reasons of adaptation or personal convenience, but is by no means identical to the individual who wears the mask.

The persona is exclusively concerned with the individual's relation to objects (people outside of herself), as opposed to her relation to the subject (her own unconscious). When we reboot the persona via therapeutic intervention, we are activating this subjective attitude, a relationship not just with the transient experience of the moment or the situation, but with our underlying connection with the soul and the collective, the transcendent.

Chapter 8

Faith Restoration—
Preparing the Soil to Sow the
Seeds of Faith Restoration

SEVERAL CONDITIONS ARE important for optimizing faith restoration and sowing the seeds of sobriety and spirituality in an addict. Cultivating simplicity is a good place to begin. The addictive process festers in chaotic minds and environments. Clearing the clutter in the physical environment is a good starting point for individuals with mental health problems in general and addictions in particular. A simple and clean environment creates a resonance of simplicity and clarity in the psyche. In Indian mythology, it is said that such environments invoke the archetype of Laxmi, the goddess of peace, prosperity, and plenty. A chaotic and unclean milieu invites her shadow twin sister, Alaxmi, the goddess of strife. Patients should simplify their living and working space before engaging in complicated undertakings of untangling the puzzle of their life problems.

Sacrifice

This calls for leaving behind old patterns and paradigms, favorite distractions, addictive diversions like having a drink, smoking a cigarette, gorging on the Internet, or food, or mindless TV watching. Maximum personal growth comes from outside the box of our habits and old modes of coping.

Spirituality

Spirit is the fuel that stokes the fire of healing and recovery. All efforts must begin with an invocation to the Spirit—the God of your understanding. The fruit of all enterprise must be turned over as offering to the divine as expressed with simple eloquence in the Lord's Prayer:

> Our Father in heaven,
> Hallowed be your name.
> Your kingdom come,
> Your will be done
> On earth, as it is in heaven.
> Give us this day our daily bread,

And forgive us our debts,
As we also have forgiven our debtors.
And lead us not into temptation,
But deliver us from evil.

In Hindu tradition, Lord Krishna counsels his protégé Arjuna thus—

Surrender all actions to me,
And fix your meditation on your inner self;
Seeking no profit,
Heedless of issue, fight the battle.

CASE STUDY:

Bob is a recovering alcoholic, in his sixties. He had wanted to restart an exercise program that had helped him maintain his sobriety in the past. He was also engaged in lots of social service whereby he was assisting other recovering addicts in his community. However, despite his desire to restart his exercise program, he was unsuccessful.

The problem was explored in a therapy session when the therapist inquired as to why he really wanted to restart exercising since he was already in active and robust recovery. He leveled with the therapist: His goal was to get "girls" interested in him. His purpose was vanity, not spiritual purposefulness. When he confronted his shadow, became conscious of his deeper motivation, and reasserted his wish to exercise to maintain his recovery and do God's work rather than "pick up women," he was successful in renewing a successful exercise program.

Sobriety

By attending to the parameters discussed above, we prepare the soil of our life for sowing the seeds of recovery. Faith in a higher order of things must be restored as we move from the horizontal axis of mundane concerns to the vertical axis of the deeper and higher priorities of life. This is the meaning of the symbol of the personal cross we must bear and claim. Authentic sobriety is only possible when this gift is reinvested into the family, community, and higher service to the Universe.

Once we have prepared the soil for faith restoration, we have found that there are additional, proactive, contemplative and spiritual practices that are helpful in faith restoration and spiritual connectedness.

Kenosis: Empty Your Cup

The most crucial intervention an addict must make to kick-start his recovery is the process of kenosis. Kenosis denotes self-emptying of one's own will and becoming entirely receptive to God's will. One cannot fill one's life with the gifts of recovery in the grace of the divine until we first empty our cup of the darkness that we carry in it. Once the cup is empty, there is room for new beginnings and the setting up of new self-structures more consistent with recovery.

Then you must empty your cup of illness and engage in behavior that makes room for wellness by recreating your consciousness with new images, energies and potentials. While it may not be possible to empty your cup all at once, or at the first attempt, you must be conscious of the importance of this task and proceed with baby steps—in small increments, one day at a time. You will gradually gain ground in your journey—a journey that calls for patience, perseverance, and persistence to combat the power of the dark side of your own nature. If you persist in this hero's journey, the healing forces of the Universe will step in to guide you on your path from illness to wellness.

Empty Cup Worksheet

Indicate which of the behaviors or symptoms you need to target:

- Complexes, hang-ups
- Character defects, including perfectionism, narcissism, histrionics, avoidance, self-defeating behavior, paranoia, withdrawal, intrusiveness, dependency
- Medical and psychiatric symptoms, including obsessions, compulsions
- Addictive behaviors towards alcohol, drugs, food, sexual activity, gambling, the Internet, pornography
- Old grudges and resentments
- Grief over old losses
- Envy
- Dysfunctional attitudes and beliefs
- Dysfunctional attachments; enmeshed and dysfunctional relationships

- Co-dependency on another for self-esteem regulation
- Goals that have outlived their purpose in your life.

Structure

The next step is to establish a simple but consistent structure for daily life and work. Individuals in early recovery should buy a week-at-a-glance calendar book. Enter each Sunday a written schedule for the coming week. This should include wake up and sleep times, times for rest, work, play, and all other activities. Then comes the matter of ranking those activities. One way is to gather critical activities into a must-do list; identify all non-essential activities and delete them; compile a list of secondary activities to be tackled only after the must-dos are completed. The must-do list should include both work and play.

Strength

Once simplicity and structure are in place, a person can muster the individual and social strength to complete the process. If he cannot do it alone, it is OK to get help from friends, relatives, and professionals. Clinicians should not be averse to supporting these efforts with appropriate and timely medication as needed to give the patient the energy and zest needed to complete the task. Special effort must be devoted to supporting the recovering addict's physical strength with a proper diet that includes fresh fruit, juices, and green teas, along with stimulating music, mild warm up exercises, and short walks. If they still don't feel up to it, advise them to fake it till they make it and as the slogan goes, "Just Do It!" The first step towards achieving your goal is to "go"!

The strength to overcome addiction comes from making a mental commitment. It activates the healing forces in the Universe to stoke the tail winds of the divine. According to Goethe:

> Until one is committed, there is hesitancy, the chance to draw back, always ineffectiveness. Concerning all acts of initiative and creation, there is one elementary truth the ignorance of which kills countless ideas and splendid plans: that the moment one definitely commits oneself, then providence moves too. All sorts of things occur

to help one that would never otherwise have occurred. A whole stream of events issues from the decision, raising in one's favor all manner of unforeseen incidents, meetings and material assistance which no man could have dreamed would have come his way. Whatever you can do or dream you can, begin it. Boldness has genius, power and magic in it. Begin it now.

Chapter 9

Contemplative Practices to Cultivate Resilience and Recovery

Pranayama

The word *pranayama* is a Sanskrit compound of the words *Prana*, or "life force," and *Yama*, meaning "Control." The word suggests the need to govern the life force within us. *Pranayama* helps us to accomplish this by breath control. On an average, each of us breathes 23,000 times a day. We take about 600 million breaths during a lifetime. You can live without food for as long as forty days and without water for seven. You can survive only six to eight minutes without air. Breath is seen as a gift of the Spirit in many traditions. Hindus believe that each breath, when engaged meditatively, is an invocation of the divine Spirit that yokes us to the numinous or the divine in the universe.

Pranayama is an essential component of the practice of yoga for centering the consciousness. *Prana* (life energy) is the gift of the universe that sustains us in this lifetime. Upon our death, our life energy merges with the cosmic or collective energy. At this point of transition, the *Atman* (individual consciousness) merges with the *Brahman* (divine consciousness). We return to the Source.

While the most immediate manifestation of *prana* is breath, ancient Indian texts classify five different types of vital energy or *pranavayus*: *prana, apana, samana, udana,* and *vyana*. These are specific manifestations of the life energy or vital wind (*pneuma*). *Prana* controls the breathing in the thoracic region. *Apana* moves in the lower abdomen and controls the elimination of urine, semen, and feces. *Samana* regulates the gastric processes aiding digestion. *Udana* operates in the throat (the pharynx and larynx) and regulates the vocal cords and the intake of food and air. *Vyana*, generally associated with the brain area, is a body-wide system of energy distribution or metabolism that distributes energy derived from food and breath through the circulatory system, while removing toxins and metabolic waste. In *pranayama*, inhalation and the *apanavayu* activate the *pranavayu* by exhalation. *Vyana* acts as mediator of *prana* and *apana* by distributing energy and removing toxic metabolites. The visible expression of this complex vital life energy in your consciousness is the movement of your lungs in respiration.

Normally *prana* is in constant association with

consciousness, which is usually driven by desire. If you can steady your *prana* (breath), you can center your consciousness and free it from desire. This freedom permits you to move from sexual and other ego desires to the spiritual realm of consciousness. When your energy body is centered, it steadies all the other *koshas*, or layers of consciousness, including the physical, emotional, and intellectual bodies. This allows you to move into your bliss body, close to your soul and Spirit—the *Atman* and the *Brahman*, the Immanent and the Transcendent.

Hindu tradition has perfected the technique of *prana*, breathing with intention and purpose. This is done by regulating inhalation *(puraka)*, exhalation *(rechaka)*, and retention of breath *(kumbhaka)*. *Puraka* infuses energy and oxygen into your body. *Rechaka* eliminates toxins. *Kumbhaka* is the energy-and toxin-management system of the *prana*. *Pranayama* must only be practiced in conjunction with *asana*, or optimal body postures, so as not to impede the flow of energy. It gives you a valuable tool to master the energy body and to center your consciousness, steadying all the other *koshas* or sheaths of your consciousness, and aligning you with your bliss body, *Atman* (soul), and the flow of the universe (Spirit).

Pranayama also offers pragmatic dividends. For instance, when your consciousness is steadied during moderate, guided breath retention, your heart rate slows, enhancing your calming, cooling, parasympathetic nervous system, as well as resting your heart muscle. This increases longevity. *Pranayama* can also alleviate pain in the physical body.

Once you are trained in basic *pranayama* techniques, you can map out your problems by circling the points on your body that are in pain. Next, establish a quiet, sacred meditative environment in a study or bedroom where you can be comfortable. Lie down on a yoga mat or a carpet, or sit up in a comfortable chair with back support. Then establish the rhythm of breath meditation and focus on the problem area of your body. While mentally focusing on this part of your body, continue your breath meditation, or *pranayama* exercise.

With each breath, you will experience a gradual diminution of pain and discomfort. Complete ten breaths while maintaining a passive focus on the problem area or painful part of your body. You will experience a 10 per cent reduction in discomfort with every breath you take.

After ten breaths, take five more. The pain or discomfort will become more relaxed as you focus on each breath. At the end of the exercise, stay calm and passive for a few more breaths before gradually returning to normal, daily consciousness. To maintain the effect of *pranayama* on your physical body, continue this practice daily for thirty minutes.

Breathing with Intention

Pranayama is to be started only after mastering the art of the *asanas*. Iyengar Yoga is a kind of postgraduate program in the Kripa Foundation. Iyengar cautions students not to attempt breathing processes until one learns how to maintain a firm diaphragm and upright spine. Later in his teaching when this was not possible to the practitioners, Guruji introduced the use of the bolster bricks, etc. (The detail protocol and guidelines for this are available in a special Yoga Guide book.)

The most fundamental *pranayama* is called *Ujjayee*. This is none other than making one's normal breath increasingly rested. Hence this can be practiced even lying down on the floor and keeping a hard cotton bolster to support the back/diaphragm. The very support helps slow down the breath and gradually increases the inhalation. Once one masters this basic *Ujayee Pranay-*

ama, one can practice the same in an upright sitting position.

The next set of *pranayama* exercises are done with the help of the fingers positioned to control the flow of breath by a single nostril. This digital method has three variations. First is *Anuloma*: this is single nostril exhalation and using both nostrils for inhalation. Second is *Pratiloma:* this is single nostril inhalation and dual nostril exhalation. The third is *Nadi shodhana*: this includes alternate nostril single nostril cyclic breathing. One breathes in by the right or the dominant, breathes out from the left or non-dominant, then breathes in from the nondominant and breathes out from the dominant. Each cycle consists of two breaths.

There are some very simple practices for a beginner or a novice who wishes to address many stress related ailments. A simple count of the inhalation and exhalation, helps one to slow down gradually erratic breathing and make it more mindful and calm with the equation of 1:2, in other words, timing the breath for one count of inhalation and two counts of exhalation. The method also could be synchronized with the "hearing" of the mantra/sacred phrase. So one counts four while one inhales and eight while one exhales. After ten such breaths, one could replace the numbers with a mantra: such as in the practice of Christian Meditation "Maranatha" (Come Lord Jesus), or the Hindu practice "Narayana." You inhale the mantra once and exhale it twice.

Use this intentional breathing technique for five to ten minutes, two or three times a day. You can also use it whenever you're feeling anxious, panicky, or in pain, if you are experiencing an addictive craving, or just to center yourself and get more focused.

Yoga, the Healing Wisdom of the Body

Saint Teresa of Calcutta used to always begin her day with a prayer, "Make us worthy, Lord, to serve those people throughout the world who live and die in poverty and hunger ..." Poverty in the non-affluent world is material poverty. But in a world gifted with affluence, she would say there is spiritual poverty and a poverty of love. She would go on to pray, "... give them through our hands this day the daily bread, the daily care they need, and by making of my life a constant life of service, in return Lord, grant me peace."

Addicts are, on the one hand, often so gifted and so extraordinarily spiritual, and yet on the other hand, so broken and so lost. This paradox is connected with the golden thread of spirituality. In working with this disease, a therapist can feel helpless and spend many hours in darkness. Like Teresa of Avila, one may question God and ask, "Why do you do such things?" God's reply: "I do these things with my friends all the time." She supposedly retorted, "No wonder you have so few friends."

Medical science has come to realize, through the work of Dr. William Duncan Silkworth of New York's Towns Hospital, that there is no chemical solution for chemical dependency. Carl Jung gave us a profound lead into the topic of spirituality and addiction. When American businessman Rowland Harrington came to him for help in the 1930s, Jung was not able to say anything to him to relieve his addiction. He told Rowland, "There is nothing in psychology to cure alcoholism." But then he also suggested that there are some who have been cured through a spiritual experience.

The 12-Step Program of Alcoholics Anonymous is connected with the golden thread of spirituality. The first step, acknowledging personal powerlessness, is the basis and the most important element of recovery. Addicts in denial often refuse to recognize their personal powerlessness. As we go through the next step, the concept of higher power emerges. It is the most essential step, taking the addict from intention to action. It emphasizes the need to shift the locus of control from the ego to the Self. Then follows the process of bringing this theory into the recovery process, to help therapists gain insight into the ways of the addict's mind.

Further on, in the fourth and fifth steps, the founding fathers of AA talked about making a searching and fearless moral inventory of oneself, inspiring the addict to take the path of self-acceptance through taking responsibility. By admitting to God, to oneself, and another human being the exact nature of what is wrong.

Following the fourth step of moral inventory and the fifth step of self-disclosure, the addict arrives at a major threshold in the recovery process. Sometimes one is confronted by the phenomenon of a dual disorder. For an addict, it can be a challenge expressed in the following words: "It's a big struggle for me to cope with addiction, and to learn that now I must also cope with a bipolar disorder or drug-induced schizophrenia! How do I handle this?" The sixth AA step expresses the need to be ready for relief of those disabilities. It leads to the seventh step, which concerns the need to seek God's help in the removal of character defects.

As an integral part of the recovery process, the last step of the 12-Steps acknowledges the principle of sharing and carrying forward the gift of recovery to others in order to maintain it for oneself. Saint Teresa practiced this powerful principle. She believed that helping while in a state of abundance was one thing, but sharing when in a state of poverty is to reach a state of grace. The 12-Step model embodies this spiritual truth beautifully. The self-help model is a paradoxical but an interesting concept. It is based on the understanding that sharing mutual vulnerability empowers the human being. God doesn't need our achievements, successes, strengths and intelligence to connect with us. God does better work with our so-called weaknesses and limitations—and, in the Christian tradition, our sinfulness. As Saint Paul puts it: "When I am weak, then I am strong … for virtue is made strong in weakness."

Harvard Medical School psychiatrist George Valiant, after studying recovering addicts who were less inclined to a "relapse syndrome," summarized the success of the AA model by identifying four catalysts for relapse prevention. They are External Conscience, Finding a substitute for destructive habits, Fellowship and love, and Spirituality and Religion. Essentially addiction is said to be a no-cure ailment requiring a safe infrastructure for maintenance. This model offers a way to reverse the addict's habits and substitute them with fellowship and love. The philosopher Martin Buber always said that we are born for love; love is an I-Thou relationship and addiction is a frustration of that; it becomes an I-it relationship. But as Saint John says, "It's not our love for God. It is God's love for us." This has to be honest and transparent.

People at various stages of life either can or cannot access that transparent honesty. That's always a dilemma while teaching meditation or other Eastern disciplines. Some people claim to believe but their solar plexus is never relaxed! Yogis have observed that if a person's solar plexus is not relaxed—though he may claim to be a believer—he is not honest about his belief. Your body never lies. Constriction in the solar plexus is the body's way of saying that one does not trust God. This physical dimension should be added to self-help programs along with the spiritual and social aspects of well-being expounded by great teachers such as Saint Teresa. With the authentic experience of God one would see the Divine in all beings and the necessity of compassion. Saint Teresa often quoted Matthew 25:40: "As long as you did it to one of the least of my brothers and sisters, you did it to me."

And interestingly, for those who know the Hindu scriptures, a similar statement can be found in the thirteth verse of the *Bhagavad Gita*. Lord Krishna says, "He who sees me in the other, in all things, the other and all things reflect me, and such a person never abandons me, and neither do I abandon such a person." This is a beautiful recipe for authentic healing.

So how does one bring that about? Saint Teresa would say that human effort is like "letting it happen." Ultimately, "God makes it happen." This transformation of the person is beyond time and space, and that's the moment of *metanoia*, which is called conversion.

The authenticity of working on so-called "cellular consciousness" made us explore what pioneering neurologist Walter Canon called the "wisdom of the body" through yoga and meditation. Using simple restorative postures specially designed to reduce the withdrawal symptoms of a recovering alcoholic, B.K.S. Iyengar developed a program used at Kripa. It progressively introduces addicts to the ways in which body, mind and soul can work together towards optimal health and the conquest of addiction. The common denominator of the ideologies of Saint Teresa and Guruji Iyengar is compassion, especially towards the poorest of the poor. Guruji taught me to reach out to the poorest of the poor, which often includes people with ailments related to addiction such as HIV AIDS.

A recovery program benefits from the combination of science and faith. The science of understanding where we came from, exploring the archetypes, and reversing the implosion of a person into an explosion of hope and recovery, is generally done via Jungian analysis which is open to the faith factor. In *The Relaxation Response*, Harvard Medical School's Herbert Benson explores the role stress plays in addiction, and helps us to find in the "relaxation response" the root of the faith factor as experienced in the human body.

CASE STUDY:

A man came into a 12-Step Program and was told that everything in recovery is achieved by the grace of God. He got turned off and was ready to leave, but the counselor said, "Hey, listen, what's your problem with your body?" He replied, "Well, I have got a bad back pain. I've got bad cervical spondylosis." The counselor said, "Okay, can I fix it for you?" After the session, the man said, "That's good. It feels so good." The counselor then explained that the body is a temple, and that what he had done just now, according to Guruji Iyengar, was a prayer that helped the man go from the periphery to the center, from the sympathetic nervous system to the central nervous system. And there we find that the center of the universe, the macrocosm, is the same center of our microcosm.

An addict stumbles through life without operating from that center because his ego is in the way. Spirituality in that sense is coming to the center.

Before he wrote *The Relaxation Response*, Benson went to the Dalai Lama in Dharamsala and based many of his findings on experiments conducted with Tibetan Buddhist monks. The simple principle of learning to relax is the invitation of the Master to come home, "Come to me, all you who labor and are overburdened, and I will give you rest" (Matthew 11:28). The whole purpose of learning relaxation is to make the faith factor authentically felt in the body.

In addressing the needs of body, mind, and spirit through yoga, start with the preliminary posture. Guruji Iyengar was a man who in his compassion reached out to the world, to multitudes of people with unexercised bodies, and devised a program to give those people a sense for the same kind of feeling that a classical yoga practitioner would get. He invented a heavy cotton bolster for use in yoga exercises. It keeps the chest and diaphragm nicely propped up. Because the posture help is given to your back ribs, the exhalation tapers down slowly. Once the exhalation tapers down, your inhalation increases. This concerns the lungs and the diaphragm. What about the heart? Because there is also a cardio-respiration where the heart muscles have to play a role. With the help of a chair you can work on this too.

Iyengar yoga and contemplative prayer share a factor in common. Intention is the basis for all other forms of prayer. But in contemplative prayer, there is no intention, just attention. That can be the most difficult thing for us to do. You don't have to do all kinds of extraordinary postures and lock yourself like a pretzel. Stay on the bolster and open up, because this will increase your cardio-respiration. It begins by working on the atrium, then working on the ventricular dimension and enhancing the inhalation, with the result that everything changes because the breath is so important.

Then we can interface the cardio-circulatory system and the cardio-respiratory system, because God has given us due wisdom to create the heart's own bypass. Cardiologists don't like to hear this. But this natural bypass via yoga can strengthen the collaterals, which is absolutely miraculous when we see it happen. Resting the calf muscles, you come into a hypometabolic condition.

And then, finally, we must attend to our posture. According to Iyengar there are two things to be aware of here: first is to find your alignment and then to find your balance. The process is always progressive, going from the beginning stage into a beautiful place where you are communicating, you are saying hello to all the major systems of your body and checking out whether they are talking to one another. And after that comes the stage of faith.

In Iyengar yoga this is the stage of faith, which has often been lost in the West. Coming to this, you realize, "I don't have to do anything." This is where God takes over. That is when you feel that there is nothing that's going on in your life that you cannot handle. This is the prayer of Thomas Merton which Saint Teresa of Calcutta said every day.

Our vocation is to discover who we are. When we've discovered who we are, the fulfilment of Augustine's prayer takes place: "Lord, help me to know myself that I may know you ... You were inside me and I was outside. You were within me and I was wandering. But you shattered my blindness and you broke through my deafness, and now I thirst for you." All of us have this thirst. This is something everyone shares with addicts. It is a dubious luxury to think that we are not prone to addiction in some form. We all have our addictions—though maybe not as glaring as the patients who come to AA or seek some other treatment.

Iyengar's Contribution to Spiritual Recovery in Addiction

B.K.S. Iyengar was a universal yogi who blended the insights of Western science with yoga. Though he passed away at the age of 95, to many of us his death was sudden. We saw him in challenging yogic postures such as *Kapotasana* until the last months of his life. As in other religious teachings, the Bible emphasizes that the body is the temple of God's Spirit. However, for Guruji this was a lived reality. Unlike in the case of many modern day yoga teachers, neither Guruji's teaching nor was his practice was a "work out." It was rather a "work-in"—a journey he always emphasized is from the periphery to the center, from the sympathetic nervous system to the central nervous system via the autonomous nervous system. Often he was like a voice in the wilderness. Many schools of yoga and even some dropouts among Guruji's students gave in to kinetic yoga and brought in all kinds of body workouts as if to compete with Western calisthenics.

Like the proverbial six blind men, many in the West took a particular aspect of Iyengar's teachings and gave it all kinds of names. Guruji was faithful to his original gift of exploring the wisdom of the body. If the body was to be revered as the temple, then every place of yogic practice (*asana*) was to become a house of prayer. His integration of the inner self *(Antaratma)* and deep meditation (*Antarang Sadhana*) in every *asana* made his practice spiritual. It is this dimension of his teaching that has helped numerous addicts understand the profundity of AA and its 12-Step Program, which has been the most successful path to healing addiction. However, while the AA program has the dimension of psycho-spirituality and psycho-social teaching, *it lacked the dimension of the psychosomatic.*

Iyengar supplied this vital dimension when he gave us the particular sequences and protocols to heal addiction and also help cope with addiction related ailments such as HIV AIDS. His holistic model of heal-ing addiction lays a major emphasis on spirituality and refers to the God of one's understanding as the Higher Power.

Since addiction is defined by Bill W. as "self-will running riot," the process of healing has to corre-spond with the fifth duty *(Niyama)* of Yoga—*Ishwara-pranidhana*—surrender to the Spirit. This can be a challenge since many alcoholics and addicts do not like any reference to God or a Higher Power. Yet in so many cases, merely keeping abstinence from alco-hol and continuing to live an egocentric life has proved counterproductive, and has been the reason for alco-holism becoming a relapse-prone ailment. Alcoholism is considered as a no cure disease similar to diabetes.

With the introduction of Iyengar yoga, a major shift from an ego-dominated personality to a self-oriented person takes place. Herbert Benson has affirmed that with yoga and meditation, a type A per-sonality can be transformed into a type B personal-ity. This is the meaning of the Greek word *metanoia*, which refers to something beyond, a profound change of mind, a radical shift in lifestyle and thought-process called conversion.

False Gods and Addiction

Alongside alcoholism and other substance abuse is a subtler but no less pervasive problem—"God addiction." In the name of God people kill. This is no different from the addict becoming violent and even committing murder to obtain the drug of his choice. It is a terrible irony that violence and terrorism are carried out in the name of God! Many people in recovery choose a religion and become self-righteous about it. In India, as well as abroad, certain ashrams and teachers are known to have encouraged the new age search for God and spirituality through the use of mind altering substances. Some who have taken up yoga have even misused this sublime discipline and invented a form of it that is called "*Ganja*-Yoga."

It is, therefore, necessary to have clear definitions of the Higher Power. Call it by any name, including God, but also caution people in recovery against being misguided by false ideas that eventually lead to disillusionment by false gods.

From a Judaeo-Christian perspective we can accuse Satan of using addiction to deviate humanity from its thirst for God. Saint Augustine of Hippo once said, "Our hearts are made for you Oh Lord, and they are restless till they rest in you." This thirst is ever present in all human beings. However, this thirst can be distracted and diverted in many ways. Alcohol is one such way. Jung warned the founders of AA that only by God's grace can one overcome the "spirit" of alcohol addiction—*"Spiritus contra Spiritum."* Unfortunately, some religious teachers have misunderstood this formula and tried substituting God for the addictive substance. Needless to say, this has proved counterproductive. Indeed, we can easily make religion, in the words of Karl Marx, "the opium of the people."

For example, when the Charismatic Center in Potta, Kerala, India, began treating alcoholics, many relapsed over and over again. The Center's founder, Father Mathew Naikamparambil, had to be literally advised to stop making God appear as some sort of a substitute for chemicals. He humbly accepted those findings and welcomed the establishment of an AA group. It is true that Jesus heals. However, to maintain that healing, one has to understand the science of addiction, accept the cross of being "disabled," and keep away from drink. Those who do not understand this and hold on to a solely "religious model" cannot maintain their recovery for long.

Addicts need to transcend any kind of "isolationist" attitude. After all, an addict is said to be living in a world with a population of one—himself. God addiction isolates people. Meditation can be a binding factor. According to Dom John Main, the founder of the World Community for Christian Meditation, "Meditation builds Communities." The Kripa Foundation uses a form of prayer in which patients of all faiths can participate. In some of Kripa's communities, even Hindu nationalists joined with other believers in meditation sessions.

In the sixth chapter of the *Bhagwad Gita*, Krishna explains to the hero Arjuna that it is necessary to transcend the world of *Prakriti* (the material world) and encounter him on the level of the *Purusha* (cosmic consciousness). This personal encounter makes the recovering person feel loved again. This is an idea mirrored in the New Testament when Saint John writes in his First Letter, that it is not our love but the love that God has for us; if one does not experience God's love through a gift of faith, our love is superficial. Many relationships break owing to the lack of this primary experience of God's love for us.

Now God's love is not something that can be earned or obtained by one's own effort. It is absolutely a gift. Hence one has to have the right kind of disposition to receive it. In Christianity, Mary comes through as a model of such love and faith. She was a contemplative at heart. The power of contemplation is that in prayer, the person is able to shift the "locus of control" from the ego to the "Indwelling Spirit of the Risen Lord." The only way our life can be managed is by giving ourselves into his hands.

In AA, the third step calls on the addict to make "a decision to turn our will and our lives over to the care of God as we understand Him." The "how" of this recommendation is in the eleventh step, where one is told to seek, through prayer and meditation, to improve our conscious contact with God. There are many kinds of prayer but contemplative prayer benefits from the involvement of the body, especially the breath. It also uses the "sound" of a word, which can become a mantra. Unlike all other forms of prayer, contemplation does not need *intention* but *attention*. God does not need our thoughts and ideas. He says clearly that it's not sacrifices or a babble of words that pleases Him but a humble and contrite heart. Mystics, especially John Cassian, Teresa of Avila, and John of the Cross, term this as "prayer of the heart" or "prayer without words." If we can incorporate such practices into treatment, it may prevent many recovering alcoholics from relapsing again and again into addiction.

When the body does not cooperate with the mind in prayer, we are filled with all kinds of distractions. This is also connected with the addictive personality's spine. There are two energies that God has created in our bodies: one is the energy of life in the spinal cord, and the other is the energy of intelligence in the brain. An addict who is filled with self-gratification generally allows this spinal energy to move downwards, triggering the urge to eat and satisfy sexual needs. The energy in the brain tends to move upwards and can lead to false pride. In prayer both these energies have to be reversed. The spinal energy must be moved upwards and the energy of intelligence downwards; both meet in the heart.

To be able to do this in the body, one has to know how to sit in meditation. When the spine is not maintained properly all kinds of distractions will result. In the Kripa Foundation's Iyengar Yoga Program, which has spread to more than forty countries, the *Sadhaka* (seeker) is taught the prayer of the heart. By unlocking the teaching of the *bandhas* in the body, which cause energy to flow without obstacles, it becomes possible to achieve a cessation of the fluctuations of the mind. In practicing this, a person becomes fully awake and "present" to the Lord. The more our society becomes a contemplative society the better will our youth turn away from addiction and other forms of self-gratification and understand the call of the Master: "If you wish to be my disciple, deny yourself, take up your cross and follow me."

The Role of Yoga and Meditation in Addiction Recovery

In 1986, Herbert Benson wrote an article for the British medical journal *Lancet* about "healing" as mind-body work. He concluded that yoga and meditation were the surest ways of changing a type A personality into a type B personality. Christians have sometimes referred to the type A personality as the "Martha syndrome." Such a person is always busy and hyperactive, preoccupied with doing things and thereby getting stressed out. Many hyperactive individuals end up becoming alcoholics.

In 1989, Benson, together with two other behavioral scientists, set up a mind-body clinic in Boston to explore healing sicknesses of the mind by working with the body. One of the experimenters, a cellular biologist, Dr. Joan Borysenko, wrote a book entitled *Minding the Body to Mend the Mind.* Her insights from the perspective of Western medical science can help to show how the body can be incorporated into AA's 12-Step Program, which makes no mention of the body. Hence in the Kripa model of recovery, we sought to introduce this pathway of healing, which we will call the psychosomatic dimension.

In India, the wisdom of the body has always been acknowledged. The work of Guruji B.K.S. Iyengar can be understood as a means to attain cellular conscious-ness. Addicts in recovery know that it is easy to say yes to a program such as AA's 12-Steps, but not to live by it. Iyengar Yoga helps one to build that motivation, not through the thinking brain (the left hemisphere), but by the "non-thinking" brain (the right hemisphere), which is activated by contemplative prayer. That is the common factor between yoga and meditation. Con-templative prayer, unlike other forms of prayer, does not need the intention of the mind but rather attention to the breath and the mantra.

Stopping the chatter of the mind is brought about by the practice of yoga and breathing exercises, which helps contemplation. The first lesson we learn from the body is that when it learns to come to rest, it is truly trusting in God. Hence, this lesson in yoga is the same as the invitation of Jesus, "Come to me all you who labor and are overburdened and I will give you rest." The area of the body that has to be specially attended to is the *Manipur Chakra* (the solar plexus). When that area is relaxed as one exhales, there is a condition medical science calls "hypo-metabolic conditioning," which helps to slow down breathing, the heart rate and, finally, brainwaves. As the Psalmist says: "Be still and know that I am God" (Psalm 46:10). Addicts are often tempted to play God, and that leads to the destruction of their lives. By contemplative prayer practiced with the help of the body through Iyengar Yoga, one learns the truth of the second step of the AA program: "Came to believe that a power greater than ourselves could restore us to sanity." Western science has affirmed the use of Iyengar Yoga in addiction treatment centers all over the world.

Iyengar Yoga and the Second and Third Steps of AA

One of the characteristics of Iyengar Yoga is that it understands the profound connection between body exercises and the practice of contemplative prayer. B.K.S. Iyengar always said, "The body is the temple of God and so every *Asana* (yoga posture) for me becomes a prayer." The common denominating factor between contemplation and Iyengar Yoga is *attention*. By focusing on breath and *mantra*, we become centered and fully in the here and now. The most difficult teaching of AA is that after admitting one's powerlessness in the first step, one is told to "believe in a power greater than one's self to restore one to sanity" and to "make one's will and life over to God." Dr. Harry Tiebout made a survey of over 500 AA members and found there were two categories of recoveries: Those who truly surrender and are faithful to the 12-Step Program and those who cannot do so. It is necessary to make the program's spiritual dimension authentic. The body-contemplative work of Iyengar Yoga as part of a recovery program provides one way to achieve this.

Recent studies in behavioral science, especially those conducted at Harvard Medical School, have affirmed the use of yoga in mind-body clinics, especially in treating stress. Many people fall into addiction owing to stress and a stress-related lifestyle. In his book that resulted from those studies, *The Relaxation Response*, Herbert Benson wrote that the effect of AA's "surrender to God" can be measured in the physical response of patients. Today, scientists are talking about a "faith factor" that can be measured bio-chemically in the production of endorphins, dopamine, and other positive neurotransmitters. This can be brought about by yoga exercises, relaxation, and the use of the mantra in meditation. Benson affirmed that yoga and meditation together activate the part of the brain governing the slowing down process. He announced at a conference on faith and healing, that "Our brain is wired to God."

Spiritual Paradox

The 12-Steps have always been called a spiritual program. It has also been clarified that while it is spiritual, it is not necessarily religious. In recent times there has been a surge of religious fundamentalism in all faith traditions. While there are those who make of the 12-Steps a completely Bible-driven teaching, there are people all over the world who follow the steps with no reference to any particular faith. What is vital is an authentic surrender to the Higher Power, which makes all the difference to the person in recovery. This involves the crushing of the ego. The "bypassing of the ego" as expressed by Dom John Main, founder of the World Community for Christian Meditation (WCCM), is the core of the practice of meditation. AA's eleventh step, which mentions prayer and meditation, offers the person a method of bringing about a *metanoia* (spiritual conversion). In recent years a similar method has been proposed by Harvard's Herbert Benson. While he began by studying the "relaxation response" to the problem of stress reduction, he went on to speak openly of the faith factor. In the second step of the 12-Steps, we find clear mention of the need to have this component in the process of recovery in the willingness to "believe."

The authenticity of this step depends on the authenticity of the first step. If instead of surrender there is only compliance, the person easily finds a variety of ways to "fake it to make it" with regard to the so-called higher power. A person in recovery must recognize and discern this crucial link between the act of surrender and seeking genuine help as suggested in the second step. Various tools of psychology are used to bring about a so-called ego-deflation that would lead a person to seek help. However, the 12-Step Program includes a psycho-social tool to bring about such a transformation. It requires an act of humility. It calls for the need to approach another person for help.

There are two unique aids that one can get within the AA program. The first is the "sponsor," someone who has walked in and out of addiction and is ready and willing to share his experience, hope, and pain with another suffering person. The second is a group of "Grateful Alcoholics" who welcome suffering alcoholics and give them a sense of belonging. This collective consciousness helps to diminish self-reliance and bring about the essential reliance on the higher power.

Meditation

When we sit in meditation we need to have a proper disposition of body and breath. The most common experience of distractions is due to lack of conditioning of the body and breath. Dom John Main teaches us to sit still and straight emphasizing that it is necessary to keep the spine upright. In yoga one directs the double energies of the body towards the heart.

This is done by two locking devices at the tail bone area and the lower abdomen. The former is called *Mulabandha* "The Root lock." The latter is called *Udhiyanabandha* "Flying up."

The energy of life moves from the base of the spine towards the heart. The other flow of energy is that of the intelligence. It descends from the brain to the heart. The chin is brought down to rest near the sternum. This is called *Jalandharabandha* (*Jala* means "net").

Thus the energy of life/spine and the energy of intelligence meet at the heart. This is the true psycho-somatic practice of the "Prayer of the Heart." Sitting erect brings about this flow of energy when one is fully in a state of "stillness."

The various postures that are adopted for conditioning one's body work on the major systems of the body: the Immune, the Nervous, and the Endocrinal. Spinal exercises help the respiration and the circulatory system. After the activation of the major systems one moves into several restorative postures that bring about the necessary hypo-metabolic condition in the body. This is evident in the slowing down of the breath, heartbeat and brainwaves.

Meditation is a private religious devotion or mental exercise in which techniques of concentration and contemplation are used to reach a heightened level of spiritual awareness. The practice has existed in all religions since ancient times. In Hinduism, it was systematized in the school of yoga. One aspect of yoga, *dhyana*

(Sanskrit for "concentrated meditation"), gave rise to a school of its own among Buddhists and became the basis of Zen. In many religions, meditation involves verbal or mental repetition of a single syllable, word, or text *(mantras)*, visual images *(mandalas)*, or devices like prayer wheels or rosaries. These can be useful in focusing concentration. In the twentieth century, secular movements like transcendental meditation emerged to teach meditation techniques outside a religious context.

There are essentially two forms of meditation: directed meditation, which focuses on a mantra (usually drawn from scripture or the sayings of a teacher), and undirected meditation, which observes whatever floats through consciousness without holding it in focus. Both forms are valuable. Focused meditation disciplines the mind to concentrate on an object of choice, ignoring all distractions, while undirected meditation disciplines the mind to detach, to let go.

The four essential elements for achieving medical benefits from meditation are the following: a quiet environment, a mental device (an object, word, sound, or image), a passive attitude (vital for evoking the relaxation response), and a comfortable position. Of these, the most important are maintaining your mental device and a passive attitude.

Just as an electrocardiogram (ECG) measures the electrical activity of the heart, doctors use the electro-encephalogram (EEG) to study the electrical activity of the brain. Recent studies in which the brain states of meditators were monitored by EEG show that those practicing undirected or mindful meditation enjoyed a conscious brain rate (called gamma activity) of 24–40 Hz per second or higher. Those practicing directed or concentration meditation relaxed their brains to calm alpha and theta states at rates of 8–12 and 4–8 Hz per second, respectively.

Measurements by EEG indicate an overall slowing of rates in the alpha and theta states subsequent to meditation, related to the proficiency of the individual's meditation practice. Neuroimaging studies indicate an increase in cerebral blood flow during meditation. Taken together, these studies seem to indicate that meditation prompts changes in the anterior cingulate cortex and dorsolateral prefrontal areas of the brain.

Imagine you are suddenly disturbed by a loud noise while reading. If the same sound is repeated a few seconds later, your attention will again be diverted from reading, only not as strongly or for as long a time. If the noise is then repeated at regular intervals, you will continue reading and become oblivious to the sound.

An auditory stimulation like a loud noise normally obliterates alpha waves for seven seconds or more. This is called "alpha blocking." However, in individuals who are not initiated in the art of meditation, the repeated sound stimulus will cease to have an impact on alpha blocking. In other words, there is a process of alpha habituation. Subjects become used to the novel stimulus once it is predictable. If the noise is repeated at fifteen-second intervals, studies find that, in normal subjects, there is virtually no alpha blocking by the fifth successive noise.

Alpha habituation persists in normal subjects for as long as the noise continues at regular and frequent intervals. In Zen masters, however, no habituation occurs. Their alpha blocking lasts two seconds with the first sound, two seconds with the fifth sound, and two seconds with the twentieth sound. This implies that Zen masters have a greater awareness of their environment as the result of meditative concentration. This capacity to stay present in a given moment and the numinosity of each experience, rather than taking it for granted, is the fundamental property of the mindfulness practiced in Buddhism. Initiates in the art of mindfulness remain acutely aware of the present moment, with its mystery and awe, and never stop celebrating the gifts of the universe. A baby's smile, a colorful tree in autumn foliage, a full moon over a lake, a lover's smile, a friend's call—these things never cease to make their hearts skip a little beat. Most of us start taking these gifts for granted and even stop noticing them. When we look at a golden tree during late fall, we may think of the impending winter rather than celebrating golden autumn.

Gamma waves are a pattern of brainwaves associated with perception and consciousness. They are produced when masses of neurons emit electrical signals at the rate of around forty times a second (40 Hz), but can often be seen between rates of 26 to 70 Hz. Researchers have recognized that higher-level cognitive activities occur when lower-frequency gamma waves suddenly double into the 40 Hz range.

EEGs picked up a much greater than normal activation of fast-moving and unusually powerful gamma waves when Buddhist monks were the subjects of study. The movement of gamma waves through their brains was far better organized and coordinated. Meditation novices showed only a slight increase in gamma-wave activity while meditating, but some of the monks produced activity more powerful than any previously reported in a healthy person.

In meditation, long-term Buddhist practitioners self-induce sustained high-amplitude gamma-band oscillations and phase-synchrony patterns. Their EEG patterns differ from non-meditators, or the "control" group people examined during these studies. In addition, the ratio of gamma-band activity (25–42 Hz) to slow oscillatory activity (4–13 Hz) is initially higher in the resting baseline before meditation for the practitioners, than it is for the control group, when measured by medial front parietal electrodes. This difference increases sharply during meditation over most of the scalp electrodes and remains higher than the initial baseline in the post-meditation baseline. This data suggests that mental training involves temporal integrative mechanisms, and may induce short-term and long-term neural changes.

It is not necessary to understand all the medical jargon here in order to appreciate the impact of these studies. Clearly, meditation has been shown to have identifiable and quantifiable physical effects, although it is too early to ascertain the clinical significance of these different EEG wave patterns in concentrated and mindful meditative states. Gamma-wave activity in mindfulness practitioners may, however, be reflective of higher states of consciousness more acutely attuned to the healing zone—where the mind can be rebooted to a healthier attitude without the cognitive distortions that can turn into physical symptoms. Conversely, once the mind is rebooted to a healthier and adaptive mode of functioning, this in turn may help reboot the body from any disease, including addiction, to a healthy threshold of functioning. This may have significant impact on the mystery of mind/body medicine in the twenty-first century. To harvest the wonders of mind/body medicine, we must take baby steps into the fluid realm where mind and matter are in a quantum state of interchangeability. Meditation offers one avenue into this realm.

Different studies cite the virtues of both concentrated and mindful meditation. For the average person, however, these distinctions are academic. The best approach is to work with the method most comfortable for you. Most meditation techniques—including transcendental meditation, the jewel of the Indian tradition—blend contemplative and concentration methods. Transcendental meditation embraces concentration on a mantra and a passive attitude to receive the healing grace of the flow of the universe.

SOBRIETY THROUGH MEDITATION

Find a quiet, solitary place in your house where you will not be disturbed for forty-five minutes.

Sit in a comfortable chair or on the floor in the Lotus position.

Make sure you are not hungry, angry, lonely, or tired (HALT).

Visualize that you are surrounded by a sphere of light. This sphere will protect you for the rest of your meditation exercise. Mentally calibrate this sphere of light to be larger or smaller until it feels right for you.

Focus on your breath with intention. Always breathe in through your nose, then gently into your tummy, then gently out again. Stay focused on your breath.

As you focus on your breath, note any distracting thoughts that come to mind. Gently put them outside of the sphere of light that protects you. Continue to focus on your breath.

With each breath, feel a gradual wave of relaxation moving from the tips of your toes, up to your ankles, gradually up to your knees and hips, then up your spine all the way to the base of your skull, and down both your shoulders, elbows, and wrists to the tips of your fingers. With successive breaths, feel the relaxation move from the base of your skull all the way to your crown and beyond.

With each subsequent breath, focus your mind on a chosen repetitive word or mantra—"peace," "relax," "joy," or any word with benign significance.

Maintain your body posture, surrounded by the sphere of protective light, and keep out all distracting thoughts. Focus on your breath with intention and reverence, gradually feeling the wave of relaxation all the way from the tips of your toes to the crown of your head. As you recite your personal mantra, continue to feel a sense of contemplative and deep relaxation.

You will gradually feel a sense of inner peace and bliss as it descends on your mind and body. Experience that inner smile from your heart.

Take five regular breaths and, with each one,

become more conscious of your body and your environment. First, feel your body, then the chair, then your body in the chair. Next, feel the chair's presence in the room, and then the presence of the room. After the fifth breath, gently open your eyes with a sense of joy and gratitude for the gift of breath, the gift of life, and the gift of the healing wisdom of the universe.

Hold the intention that you will use these gifts to reach your best personal potentials, and that you will use these potentials in the service of family, community, and the God of your understanding. They will help you enter the healing zone.

Mindfulness

Mindfulness means being aware of the presence of the sacred and the divine order all around us. This allows us to make a direct, vital, and living connection with the divine. This implies centering our consciousness, quieting the monkey mind, and stabilizing the different Koshas or sheaths of consciousness.

The Hindu tradition calls for stabilizing the four levels of consciousness that impede our connection with the divine in and around us. These include body, breath, thinking, and feeling. Once these are stabilized, it is said that we are in our bliss body. The bliss body connects us with our soul *(Atman)*, which is in direct communion with the primal spirit *(Brahman)*.

Mindfulness is the active awareness of body, feelings, and thoughts, and your perception of objects, events, and individuals in your environment. It is the capacity to connect with the true nature of inner and outer reality without the distortions caused by the veil of *maya* through which you perceive others, the world, and yourself. This veil is created by distortions in your body, your thoughts and your feelings, and in your perception of self, others, and the world. When you see the world through the veil of *maya*, your perceptions are transient and lead to suffering caused by your attempts to chase pleasure and avoid pain. Through mindfulness, you can realize that your perceptions mire you in your ego and disconnect you from the transcendent reality of soul and Spirit.

Buddha provided a guide to mindfulness over 2,500 years ago. The Four Noble Truths of Buddhism include the truth of suffering, the truth of the cause of suffering, the truth of the end of suffering, and the truth of the path that leads to the end of suffering. Suffering is an aspect of the human condition; its cause is attachment to *samsara*, or life. The end of suffering, or *Nirvana*, entails a state of non-attachment or detachment. This state helps you attain *Sunyata*, or the sacred void that makes room for what the Christian tradition calls kenosis—emptying the cup of your life and moving beyond superficial strivings. This in turn allows the divine, or Spirit, to emerge through a spiritually purposeful or dharmic life. The fourth Noble Truth charts the method for attaining the end of suffering. Buddhists call this the Noble Eightfold Path. Once you attain this spiritual attitude through mindfulness, you experience the true nature of reality and the divine in the present moment. This connects you to your sober core.

The steps on the Noble Eightfold Path are these: right understanding, right thought, right speech, right action, right livelihood, right effort, right mindfulness, and right concentration. "Right" here implies following the guidance of your soul rather than doing the bidding of your ego and your complexes—the shadow, or lower, aspects of your personality.

Mindfulness involves engaging in the present moment rather than remaining trapped in the past or being seduced by the future. By engaging in the present moment, you begin to see both inner and outer aspects of reality more accurately, devoid of the distortions of past experiences or future expectations. The present moment is the sacred realm that connects your history with your spiritual destiny.

Another important dimension of practicing mindfulness is that it moves you from the experiencing ego to the observing consciousness. In so doing, you become an impartial but caring witness to your own experiences and body sensations, thoughts and feelings, rather than becoming one with them. Through this, you learn that when you are angry, you are not a bundle of anger. When you have neck pain, you are not the pain. If you have cancer, you are not the cancer; a part of your body has the cancer. This realization permits you to ally with the rest of your being as a witness to the whole picture rather than merging with the disease or dysfunctional part.

In practicing mindfulness, you realize that body sensations, thoughts, and feelings—and your perceptions of self, others, and the objects in your environment—are transient; they create impermanent states of pain or pleasure and are temporary constructs of your ego, rather than stable attributes of your soul. You are free to release a body posture, a breathing irregularity, a thought distortion, or a faulty perception of others, when you realize that these momentary experiences are not enduring, stable realities of your soul. Rather, they are part of a world view you construct with your ego to pursue pleasure and avoid suffering. In mindfulness, you are free to observe life without getting caught in ego distortions.

As you observe inner reality more closely, you will find that happiness is not exclusively a quality brought about by a change in outer circumstances; it comes through centering yourself on your soul's guidance. Joy stems from loosening and releasing attachment to your hang-ups or complexes, which are the distorted lens through which you see the world. For example, if you have an inferiority complex, you assign tremendous power to others and relinquish your own authority. With a superiority complex or narcissistic personality, you inflate your own power and minimize the contribution of others in your life. Neither state is healthy or in tune with the larger reality of life.

Mindfulness does not have to be constrained to a formal meditation session. It is an activity that can be done at any time using *pranayama*, or breath management. Benedictine, Jain, Buddhist, Eastern Orthodox, and Hindu monks often practice a walking meditation and mindfulness. Any activity done mindfully is a form of meditation, and mindfulness is possible at practically any time.

In mindfulness, you focus on whatever activity you have undertaken with intention, deliberation, and total attention to every posture and movement. Instead of taking a "jitterbug" approach, you must slow down your activity by giving attention to every detail of your movement. If you are walking, feel Mother Earth supporting you with every step. If you are washing your car, feel the warmth of the water, the soft sponge, the sleek car, the cleansing soap, and the beautiful sunshine on your skin as you work. Be aware of your posture as you carry on the activity. Is your posture alert, flowing with the activity? Or is it rigid? Does the activity of your body cause you pain or pleasure? Remind yourself that whatever you are feeling in your body is transient and impermanent. Any attempt to avoid pain and seek pleasure is going to anchor your body to the illusionary or the transient. When you realize this transience, you can free your body and posture to align with the guidance of your soul and the intention of Spirit in the present moment. Your body then becomes an instrument of the Spirit.

When you engage in body mindfulness, any activity

becomes a yoga exercise connecting you with the flow of the healing energy of the universe. You can then experience the vein of joy and bliss beyond the discomfort of your body and the posture you are in. You can focus on the purpose your body has undertaken in the present rather than focus on your body itself.

When you undertake a mindfulness exercise—walking, sitting, or eating—focus on your breath. Is your breath regular or irregular? Slow or rapid? Rhythmic or chaotic? Nasal or oral? Are you breathing from your chest or from your abdomen? Is your breathing intentional or unconscious? Notice whether you can maintain focus on your breath—or if your mind jumps to other thoughts, images, feelings, or events.

The goal of breath mindfulness is to anchor your awareness to your breath. Your breathing should be slow and steady, systematic and nasal; breathe through your abdomen. Breathe without exertion, embracing all four steps of breathing—inhalation, abdominal retention of breath, exhalation and external retention of breath—pacing each step to a count of three.

When your breath becomes unsteady, remind yourself that whatever distracts you is transient and will pass. If you are trying to perpetuate some pleasure or avoid pain, remind yourself that pain and pleasure are both impermanent, and that chasing them only causes suffering. When you filter out these distractions, your breath will be steadied and will align with a deeper consciousness. It will become ready to join the flow of the universe and become a vehicle of the soul to do the work of the Spirit. Breath mindfulness is one of the fastest and most expedient ways to center your monkey mind on a mindfulness track.

In dealing with addicts or other patients in great pain or stress, a therapist can center himself by focusing on his own breath. This makes for a more helpful bodily and mental mindset with which to respond to the patient. Patients can be invited to stay centered on their own breathing if they become anxious, panicky, dissociative, or emotionally fragmented when dealing with traumatic memories.

Inevitably, when practicing mindfulness, objects and individuals surround you. Some are experienced as pleasurable; others are painful. Some are desirable; some are disgusting. Usually, these perceptions, which are based on past experiences or future expectations, spin a veil of Maya, or distortion, over your perceptions. The goal of mindfulness is to suspend judgment and anchor your perception in the present moment within a neutral frame—detached from pain or pleasure, desire or disgust. You must accept that whatever your perception of an individual or event may be, it is transient and it too shall pass. Remind yourself that your perception is just a fleeting X-ray of an impermanent situation; that it is not the same as it was yesterday, and will not be the same tomorrow.

If an event, object, or individual calls for a response in the moment, respond in an authentic, sincere, and detached manner to accomplish the task at hand—and then let go. If a friend drives you in his lovely sports car, enjoy the ride to your destination; do not get caught in admiration or envy of the friend and plan to acquire a similar or better car as soon as possible. With mindfulness, individuals and objects become vehicles of the soul, not the center of your desire.

This detached attitude helps you respond to the present moment so that you can deal with outer reality, yet be free to investigate the present in a deeper context, and reflect on the more enduring or permanent aspects of the situation. This is the archetypal meaning of the present that shows how this moment fits into the larger script of your life—your spiritual purpose, your dharma. It helps you put the moment in perspective and tunes you into the dharmic or spiritual flow of your life, opening you to the energy flow of the universe. You can feel this in others who are guided by a sense of spiritual purpose. These individuals are old souls that have a certain unconscious aura about them. They attract us and make us feel good about the world and ourselves. Stay close to these people. Veterans of the 12-Step Program speak of this as "sticking with the winners."

Reflective, spiritually energized mindfulness opens up a vein of joy in your daily enterprise and lets you detach from the moment-to-moment pursuit of pleasure and avoidance of pain, encouraging you instead to dance to the deeper rhythm of life. Tuning in to your bliss body, soul, or *Atman* gives your consciousness a sharper focus. You can learn to manage the affairs of everyday life, while stepping back from them in favor of the deeper currents of your spiritual life. The experience is rejuvenating and health-restoring.

In practicing mindfulness, you experience a void in your ego consciousness from the absence of the ego's ceaseless chatter—the cause of your restlessness. We often confuse the serenity of the void with boredom. Only the initiated understand that the void is the sacred space that old souls try so hard to establish.

If you are bored with sitting still in mind and body, even for a short time, consider this: you are a passenger on Mother Ship Earth. The earth is spinning at about 1000 miles per hour at the equator and revolves at 66,000 miles per hour around the sun. The Sun and the Earth are moving at 48,300 miles per hour within the Milky Way and our galaxy is moving at 1.3 million miles per hour within the universe. If you can honor the void, you may experience the energy of the momentum of the universe flow through you!

It takes tremendous courage and integrity to be true to your own nature. If you are practicing mindfulness and your mind strays to thoughts of making love to an attractive person, acknowledge your thought, your sensual nature, and guide it from lust to a soulful assessment of how you can transform your sensual nature from objectifying the person to relating to him or her as an individual soul—a living creature of God with a unique purpose in this lifetime. This does not negate your healthy attraction, but puts it into a larger spiritual context. You may find that this person attracts you beyond simple lust; perhaps grace and inner beauty beckon to you. For men, this may prompt you to explore which part of your hidden grace and beauty the woman embodies and how you can live out this unlived part of your *anima*, or inner sacred feminine.

Mindfulness permits you to experience the moment

in its full numinosity and engage the magic in the moment, whether it involves a pretty flower, a playful child, or a stranger's smile.

The experiencing ego is a function of the outer ego consciousness; the inner witness is a function of the soul. When these two do their dance, the resultant rhythm creates the music of mindfulness. I call this observing consciousness the "eagle consciousness," because it grants us an eagle's eye-view of ourselves. The sacred eagle is the totem bird for the observing consciousness.

Human consciousness is defined by the capacity to make choices. We can choose change or the status quo. One of the great human dilemmas involves balancing change with acceptance. Change must be guided by your soul and your spiritual path, rather than by self-interest alone. However, you will always reach a crossroad where you will ask yourself: Should I struggle to change my situation or accept it? Mindfulness is a great guide at this crossroad. You should push for changes only when they are in harmony with your spiritual purpose. If this is not the case, you should accept your situation, trusting in God and the universe. This attitude moves you from dry drunk to a sober, spiritually engaged, and purposeful, life. In the Hindu

Scriptures, the *Bhagwad Gita*, Lord Krishna counsels his protégé Arjuna on the yogic wisdom of engaging a spiritually purposeful, fully-engaged life, with detachment and mindfulness. "Work other than that done as a selfless service binds human beings," Krishna said. "Therefore, becoming free from selfish attachment to the fruits of work, do your duty efficiently as a service to Me."

The daily mindfulness exercise—given below—is designed to give you a soul's eye-view of yourself in contrast to the ego's view. In daily life—caught in addiction, in the ego's chatter and concerns, and in the horizontal axis of your existence—you have little time for reflecting on the bigger picture. You devote little time to charting the sacred undercurrent of your existence, the meaning of your mundane life in the larger scheme of things. You are hard pressed to attend to your life in the context of family, neighborhood, city, country, and humanity.

When you are mindful of the eagle's view of yourself, you can realign your daily life with its eternal dimension and your momentary preoccupations with the eternal flow of life. Your finite existence can join with the infinite and absolute as best you understand it. Every moment, as mundane and trivial as it may seem, will then be infused with the purpose and the guidance of the sacred and its plan for you. When this bigger picture guides you, you feel focused, aligned, healthy, and whole. This feeling is the source of vitality and rejuvenation for your mind, body, and soul.

You will know that you are in this highly numinous state of consciousness when you experience a vein of joy coursing through your being. When sustained for long enough, this joy permeates your mind, your body, and your soul with a sense of bliss that transcends individual consciousness and raises you into the collective consciousness. You will feel one with the universe. Freud described this as an "oceanic feeling." Jung called it the *Unus Mundus*. The ancient Hindu sages and *rishis* called this deeply blissful state *Samadhi*. This treasure is hard to attain. But with patience, practice, reverence, guidance, and wisdom, each of us has the potential to glimpse the sacred and numinous flow of sobriety.

Practicing Mindfulness

When you do a mindfulness exercise in the context of aligning your thoughts, feelings, and actions to your soul, you are likely to harvest optimal health and spiritual dividends. Many researchers have outlined excellent exercises for attending to the practice of mindfulness. Here is a simple one that has proven helpful.

MINDFULNESS EXERCISE

Begin at a quiet time and in a secluded, comfortable place in your home. With experience, the practice of mindfulness can occur anywhere, at any time, and with any activity.

Once you've secured a clean, quiet and simple environment, then shut off all distractions, especially the cell phone, and create a quiet shaded environment by turning off the lights. This provides an optimal circadian matrix for your mindfulness practice.

Sit either on the ground in the lotus position or in a comfortable chair with the back straight, feet firm on the ground. Fold your hands in front of you, facing upwards toward the sky, so that you are in a receptive posture to receive the blessings of the grace of divine consciousness and the gifts of recovery and healing. It is ideal to wear loose-fitting clothing, preferably white or light colors. These are more conducive to inviting the sacred energy and the positive vibrations from the universe. This posture stabilizes your physical body; in the Hindu tradition this is stabilizing your *Anamaya Kosha* sheath of consciousness.

Once you stabilize your physical body, it is time to stabilize your breath body. This is accomplished by breathing gently through your nose, into your stomach, holding the breath in your tummy for a count of two, and then gently breathing out through the nose. Continue this breath cycle repetitively. This regulates your breath; nasal breathing is eminently healthier than oral breath. Holding the breath in the stomach allows for the oxygen to diffuse into your tissues, and for carbon dioxide and other toxins to be diffused into the venous blood for detoxification via the lungs, skin, and other organs of excretion. Breathing into the stomach calms the parasympathetic nervous system and invokes the relaxation response. It enhances the blood levels of acetylcholine and oxytocin, both essential for optimal functioning of our nervous system and our attachment matrix. For the rest of the mindfulness practice, continue to breathe with intention in the method discussed above. This stabilizes your breath body or the *Pranamaya Kosha* sheath of consciousness.

Make sure that your body is still in the optimal meditative posture that we have established, and that you are attending to your intentional breath. Having stabilized your physical body and the breath body, now be aware of your thinking processes. Become an observer to the thoughts visiting you at this moment. Thank your thoughts for visiting. Tell them that at the present time you have a date with the divine. Respectfully put your visiting thoughts into a box outside of your body and tell them that you will attend to them after you have completed your mindfulness practice. Then continue to maintain your body and your breath mindfulness. By respectfully putting the visiting thoughts outside of you, you feel that your thoughts are now not distracting you. This esstabilizes your thinking body or the *Vignanmaya Kosha* sheath of consciousness.

Having stabilized your physical, breathing and thinking bodies, and maintaining your body posture and breath mindfulness, observe how you are feeling in this present moment. Are you feeling mad, glad, sad, afraid, shameful, or guilty? All other feelings are but a combination and permutations of these six basic feeling states. Acknowledge what you're feeling. Respectfully tell your feelings that you will attend to them after you have completed your mindfulness practice. And then put these feelings in the same box as your thoughts for later attention. This clears your consciousness of any distracting feelings, besides stabilizing your feeling body, or your *Manamaya Kosha* sheath of consciousness.

Now that you have learned to stabilize your physical body, your breath body, your thinking and feeling bodies, and as you continue to regulate your mindfulness exercise, you will gradually feel a sense of joy or bliss in your heart. This comes from an uninterrupted sense of connection with the sacred and the divine in the moment. This is your bliss body. Acknowledge the sense of joy and bliss that you're feeling. However, as joyful as bliss is, it too is a distraction from your direct and intimate connectedness with the divine. Respectfully let go of a sense of place and detachment, thus feeling a deeper, purer sense of consciousness. This thus stabilizes your bliss body or your *Anandamaya Kosha* sheath of consciousness.

Now that you have stabilized your physical body, your breath body, your thinking and feeling bodies, as well as your bliss body, you will feel a sense of your own depth as you descend into your deepest consciousness. It is being in your soul. For Hindus this is being in your *Atman* consciousness. This is the place closest to the divine, a place without interruptions from the outer ego layers of consciousness. At this point your soul is in direct communion with the sacred, with the Spirit. Your *Atman* is now more directly connected to the *Brahman* or the universal consciousness. We vibrate in sync with the rest of God's universe. This is the experience of pure consciousness. This resets and reboots the mind-body relationship, and all our relationships, to a more sober and optimal frequency. Feel the sense in the presence of the sacred in and around you. Let it heal your mind, body and spirit. Keep this place of spiritual connectedness for 10 to 15 minutes.

Now gradually return to your outer consciousness as follows: Firstly, be aware of the breath that breathes through you and continues to breathe. Next, be aware of your body and continue to breathe. Then be aware of the chair that holds your body and continue to breathe in a slow and intentional manner. Next be aware of the room that holds the chair that holds the body and continue to breathe. Remember, at the present time your health is in the hands of God who holds the room, which holds the chair that holds your body that continues to breathe, aware of and gratified for the gift of breath, the gift of life, and the gift of sobriety. Sincerely intend to use God's gifts wisely to achieve your best personal potentials, and to put these potentials to use in the service of your family, your community, and to do God's work. Then gradually open your eyes respectfully, first consciously looking down at great Mother Earth with gratitude for being your home from birth through death. Continue to breathe. Then with open eyes, respectfully look up at the ceiling, the sky, with gratitude for the protection of the Holy Spirit during your brief tenure on this planet and continue to breathe. Then gradually connect to the outer consciousness. After sitting still for a few more minutes, gradually resume your normal day.

This concludes the mindfulness practice but mindfulness should become not just an exercise but a way of life. Choose an activity during which you will practice mindfulness. This may be one of any number of things—going for a walk alone, eating a meal, organizing the desk or closet, cleaning the garage, mowing the lawn, doing the dishes, or preparing a meal. Slow down the pace of the activity and do it with some degree of deliberation. Instead of rushing through the activity, do it intentionally, slowing your body and using systematic, methodical, intentional movements.

Epigenetic Impact of Mindfulness

Epigenetics is the study of changes in organisms caused by modifications in gene expression rather than alteration of the genetic code itself.

Epigenetics literally means "above" or "on top of" genetics. It refers to external modifications to DNA that turn genes "on" or "off." These modifications do not change the DNA sequence, but instead, they affect how our cells "read" our genes.

Epigenetic changes alter the physical structure of DNA. One example of an epigenetic change is DNA methylation—the addition of a methyl group, or a "chemical cap," to part of the DNA molecule which prevents certain genes from being expressed.

Another example is histone modification. Histones are proteins that DNA wraps around. (Without histones, DNA would be too long to fit inside cells.) If histones squeeze DNA tightly, the DNA cannot be "read" by the cell. Modifications that relax the histones can make the DNA accessible to proteins that "read" genes. Studies have shown that mindfulness meditation decreases inflammatory epigenetics. In other words, mindfulness has anti-inflammatory potential.

Mindfulness Meditation & Telomeres

What is a telomere? Our chromosomes contain genetic material in the form of strands of DNA. Telomeres are extensions of these DNA strands that protect the integrity of the DNA. Telomeres are sort of like those plastic tips that cover and protect the end of shoelaces from fraying. Telomeres tend to get shorter as we age. Evidence suggests telomere length is a reliable indicator of overall health. Short telomeres are associated with increased health risk factors.

Mindfulness meditation increases telomere integrity and longevity and overall health in diverse groups, including breast cancer survivors.

Chapter 10

Living Your Personal Myth

EVERY INDIVIDUAL LIVES by her or his personal myth. A myth is an archetypal pacemaker of our soul—the lens through which we look at ourselves and at others, at the world and the future. It could be the myth of the mother, father, warrior, lover, trickster, leader or mentor, or the myth of the alchemist creating new possibilities.

For every addict and every individual, it is important to be aware of your personal myth and to live it optimally. At times, an individual may be living an outdated myth, or living on the wrong side of the coin of his myth. For example, an addict may be caught in the myth of an orphan in search of a mother rather than live the myth of the lover, which may be more appropriate for his life stage. Such individuals will regress to a mother/child encounter with their lover rather than adult love. When we are living an outdated myth, or living the wrong side of the myth, we trigger dissonance in our psyche that manifests as addictive cravings for a more optimal myth. This mismatch manifests as addiction or a host of medical or psychiatric problems, relationship tangles, and character issues or hang-ups or complexes.

Case Study: Virgo's Journey

Virgo was a physician troubled by drug addiction, marital problems, depression and burn-out in his profession. He was the only child of Northern European parents, who doted on him. He was a virtuous son who wanted to be an aviator, but chose to be a physician after the expectations of his parents. He was a lover and poet at heart who lived the gruelling grind of the medical profession, disconnected from his passion for culture and the arts. He once saw a painting called "Cupid Chastised" at the Chicago Art Museum during a school outing. He forgot about this image, till he ran into it as an adult while in analysis. It had a deep impact on him. He said that he instinctively felt that it was his story.

The image depicts the god of war Ares whipping Eros, the god of love. Venus intercedes on Eros' behalf to protect him. He identified with Eros, while he was living the myth of Ares—driven to succeed in the professional realm. Eros was the myth of the lover, the poet, roles that had been marginalized in his life. Venus, his anima and feeling function, intervened to restore the balance between the Eros and Ares aspects of his personal myth. He married a soulful women, worked part time, and made room for arts, music, poetry, and friendships. He is maintaining his long-term sobriety and sustained recovery. His analysis was focused on transformation of his personal myth from Ares, god of war, to Eros, god of love.

CASE STUDY: KATHERINE'S ODYSSEY

Katherine, a woman in her late forties, had endured two difficult divorces. Both ex-husbands had addiction issues and she had co-dependency traits. She sought therapy because she wanted to make a more enduring choice of a mate and avoid past errors in her relationships. She was also a successful community volunteer and advocate in her community. The choice of the right man was the major focus of her initial therapy. Then she had the following dream:

I have applied for admission to three courses in fairy tales at the local university. I got admis-

sion in two of the three classes, but the third class that I really want to attend is full. This is the class concerning the fairy tale of the Velveteen Rabbit. I am disappointed.

This dream became a major turning point in her recovery from codependency. The dream indicated that the Velveteen Rabbit story was a "Do Not Enter" myth for her. This story is about a toy rabbit that comes to life when the boy loves and accepts him. The dream indicated that she must not enter this maze of seeking a man's love to feel alive and whole. Rejecting the idea that only the love of a man can make her feel whole, she was able to tune into her own inner resources to validate herself. Now, the relationship with a man became a wish, not a need. This freed her to live out her own potentials and seek a relationship without the compulsion to make it work as her survival tool.

In this inner work, Carl Jung struggled with the question of his own personal myth.

So I suspected that myth had a meaning which I was sure to miss if I lived outside it in the haze of my own speculations. I was driven to ask myself in the seriousness: "What is the myth you are living?"

What was Jung's personal myth? He started out his early life trajectory under the guidance of the Hero Myth. He became the son and crown prince of Sigmund Freud's movement, which led to a degree of enmeshment and co-dependence. He derived his sense of self-worth and validation from affirmation from Freud. Eventually, in his inner work, he had to kill within himself the Hero Myth symbolized by Siegfried. Upon the culmination of his inner journey, Jung reached the peak of his individuation under the auspices of his ultimate personal myth, the archetype of the teacher: the Wise Old Man Philemon.

Faith Restoration

The core dynamic of additive thinking is a reliance on another individual for a sense of validation and well-being. When this hunger for being deemed adequate and loveable by another is frustrated, as it usually is, the addict becomes emotionally fragmented and falls into his addiction of choice to self-soothe and restore his illusion of self-esteem. What he is unable to do is to have faith in turning to the God of his understanding for guidance and validation.

Saint Augustine struggled with this issue and came up with clear guidance for teaching a pertinent lesson: only in the presence of the Omnipotent and the Omniscient can the self attain happiness and completeness.

Augustine was reading the letters of Saint Paul, and let the book fall open on its own. He was astonished to read Romans 13:13, where Paul exhorts his readers to give up the way of the senses and walk the path of Christ. Augustine chose to heed Paul's advice.

He chose the soul over the body, the intellect over desire, faith over questioning, and reason over uncertainty. In *The Confessions*, Augustine single-handedly creates a theology of the self—a total, complete view of the self in relation to God.

This certainly has been our clinical experience. When an addict's faith is restored, he is able to get it right: God first, himself second, and everyone else after that.

The Latin axiom, "*Vocatus Atque non Vocatus Deus Advenit*" ("Bidden or unbidden, God will be there") captures the essence of faith restoration. We are always surrounded by the sacred, the divine, even when we are not consciously aware of it. Every breath we take is an evidence of the benevolence and the grace of the divine, gifting us life, health, and joy.

However, the degree of our physical and mental health, the depth of our recovery and sobriety, the robustness of our relationships, are all directly proportional to the extent that we are consciously connected with this universal healing energy, the *Brahman*, the Primal Spirit. When this connection is anemic, we are ill; when this connection is robust, we are well.

In this book, we have offered some contemplative practices that help us to restore a conscious, vital, active connection with this healing Sprit.

Join us in celebrating this life-giving force.

Appendix A

Neuroscience of Resilience

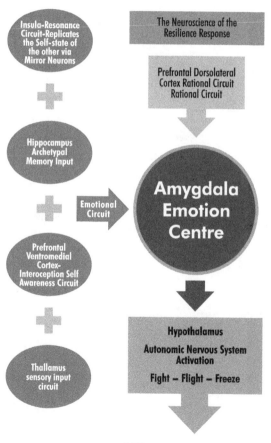

Appendix B

Rapid Emotional Circuit

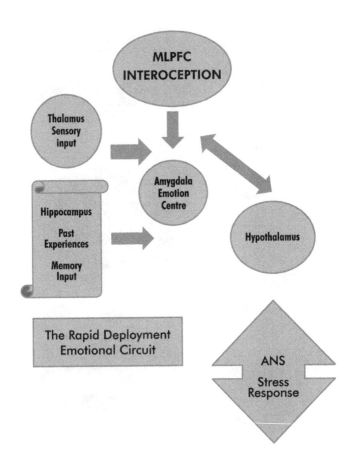

Appendix C

Second Rational Response Circuit

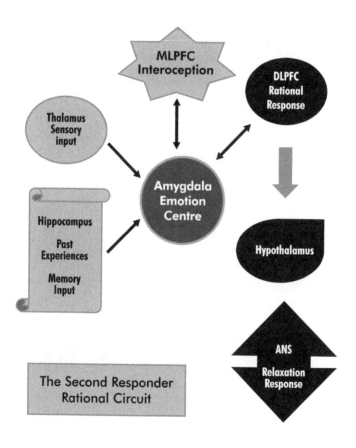

Appendix D

Resonance Bluetooth Circuit

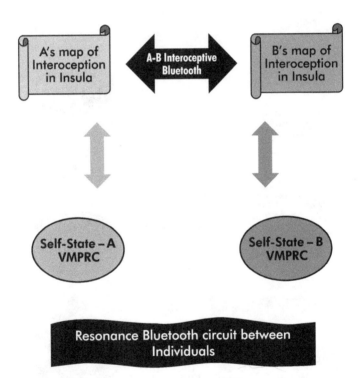

Appendix E
The Transcendent Function

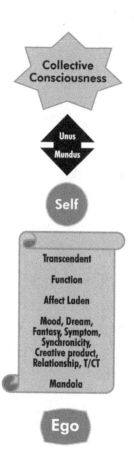

Collective
Consciousness

Unus
Mundus

Self

Transcendent

Function

Affect Laden

Mood, Dream,
Fantasy, Symptom,
Synchronicity,
Creative product,
Relationship, T/CT

Mandala

Ego

Acknowledgments

THIS BOOK WAS inspired by Usha Bedi (Ashok's better half!). She was our muse and she motivated the coauthors to expand their discussions into this book on the vital subject of faith deficit.

In India, Krishna Iyer was instrumental in keeping us organized and on track with the editorial support and structure to get the tail winds to the project.

Material from the 12-Step Program is reprinted with permission of Alcoholics Anonymous World Services, Inc. (AAWS). Permission to reprint the 12-Steps does not mean that AAWS has reviewed or approved the contents of this publication, or that AAWS necessarily agrees with the views expressed herein.

A.A. is a program of recovery developed for alcoholism only. Use of the 12-Steps in connection with programs and activities which are patterned after A.A., but which address other problems, or in any other non-A.A. context, does not imply otherwise.

We are grateful to Dr. Lance Longo for his generous contribution to our understanding. We are grateful to our patients for sharing their stories so that we may learn and grow from them. Also, our gratitude to patients and staff both at the Dewey Center for Addiction Recovery in Milwaukee and from all the centers of recovery under the auspices of the Kripa Foundation around the world. We also acknowledge the researchers whose work has enlightened the scientific basis of addiction and recovery.

Gratitude to Brian Mascarenhas of Santosh Yoga for introducing the authors to each other. Many thanks to David Luhrssen for his assistance in editing the book and making it accessible to a wider readership without losing its academic integrity.

Finally, we extend our apologies to anyone who has been inadvertently omitted from our acknowledgments and references.

Bibliography

1. James W: The Varieties of Religious Experience. USA, Penguin Classics, 1982

2. Wilson B, Jung CG: Bill W—C.G. Jung correspondence. AA Grapevine–the International Journal of Alcoholics Anonymous 1978; 35:26-31

3. Jung CG: The Structure and Dynamics of the Psyche, Volume 8. Princeton, N.J., Princeton University Press, 1969

4. Alcoholics Anonymous World Services, Inc: Big book on line 2013; 2013

5. Edited by Grof S.), Grof C: Spiritual emergency: When personal transformation becomes a crisis (new consciousness readers), Edited by Grof S, Grof C. USA, Grof, Stanislav (Editor); Grof, Christina (Editor), 1989

6. Wolfgang von Goethe, Johann (Author), Hamlin, Cyrus (Editor), Arndt, Walter W. (Translator): Faust: A Tragedy (Norton Critical Editions) [Paperback] Second Edition. W.W. Norton & Company, 1998

7. Edinger EF: Goethe's Faust: Notes for a Jungian Commentary (Studies in Jungian Psychology by Jungian Analysts). Toronto, Canada, Inner City Books, 1990

8. Jung CG: The Practice of Psychotherapy: Essays on the Psychology of the Transference and Other Subjects, Volume 16. Princeton, N.J., Princeton University Press, 1966

9. Edinger EF: Ego and Archetype: Individuation and the Religious Function of the Psyche. Boston, Mass., Shambhala, 1992

10. Hawthorne N: the Scarlet Letter. CreateSpace Independent Publishing Platform, 2013

11. Badii F: Symptoms related to addiction: Elements for the differential diagnosis with personality disorders. Riv Psichiatr 2013; 48:370-374

12. Casadio P, Olivoni D, Ferrari B, Pintori C, Speranza E, Bosi M, Belli V, Baruzzi L, Pantieri P, Ragazzini G, Rivola F, Atti AR: Personality disorders in addiction outpatients: Prevalence and effects on psychosocial functioning. Subst. Abuse 2014; 8:17-24

13. Ghafarinezhad A, Rajabizadeh G, Shahriari V: Relationships of dissociative disorders and personality traits in opium addicts on methadone treatment. Addict Health 2013; 5:21-26

14. Gonzalez C: Screening for personality disorder in drug and alcohol dependence. Psychiatry Res 2014; 217:121-123

15. Kienast T, Stoffers J, Bermpohl F, Lieb K: Borderline personality disorder and comorbid addiction. Dtsch Arztebl Int 2014; 111:280-286

16. Mitchell MR, Potenza MN: Addictions and personality traits: Impulsivity and related constructs. Curr Behav Neurosci Rep 2014; 1:1-12

17. Reas DL, Ro O, Karterud S, Hummelen B, Pedersen

G: Eating disorders in a large clinical sample of men and women with personality disorders. Int J Eat Disord 2013; 46:801-809

18. Rentrop M, Zilker T, Lederle A, Birkhofer A, Horz S: Psychiatric comorbidity and personality structure in patients with polyvalent addiction. Psychopathology 2014; 47:133-140

19. King James Bible Online: King James Bible online Matthew Chapter 6:10. 2013

20. Jung CG, Jaffé A: Memories, Dreams, Reflections. London, Collins and Routledge & Kegan Paul, 1963

21. Jung CG: Mysterium Coniunctionis: An Inquiry into the Separation and Synthesis of Psychic Opposites in Alchemy, Volume 14. Princeton, N.J., Princeton University Press, 1970

22. Bennett DA, Schneider JA, Buchman AS, Mendes de Leon C, Bienias JL, Wilson RS: The rush memory and ageing project: Study design and baseline characteristics of the study cohort Neuroepidemiology 2005; 25:163-175

23. Bennett DA, Wilson RS, Schneider JA, Evans DA, Mendes de Leon CF, Arnold SE, Barnes LL, Bienias JL: Education modifies the relation of AD pathology to level of cognitive function in older persons Neurology 2003; 60:1909 <last_page> 1915

24. Boyle PA, Barnes LL, Buchman AS, Bennett DA: Purpose in life is associated with mortality among com-

munity-dwelling older persons Psychosom Med 2009;
2009; 71:574 <last_page> 579

25. Boyle PA, Buchman AS, Bennett DA: Purpose in life
    is associated with a reduced risk of incident disability
    among community-dwelling older persons Am J Geriatr
    Psychiatry 2010

26. Boyle PA, Buchman AS, Wilson RS, Yu L, Schneider
    JA, Bennett DA: Effect of purpose in life on the relation
    between alzheimer disease pathologic changes on cog-
    nitive function in advanced age [original article] Arch
    Gen Psychiatry 2012; 69:499-504

27. Brulin C, Gustafson Y, Hedberg P: Purpose in life
    among men and women aged 85 years and older The
    International Journal of Ageing and Human Develop-
    ment 2010; 2010; 70:213 <last_page> 229

28. Martin RA, Mackinnon S, Johnson J, Rohsenow DJ:
    Purpose in life predicts treatment outcome among adult
    cocaine abusers in treatment J Subst Abuse Treat 2010

29. McKnight PE, Kashdan TB: Purpose in life as a system
    that creates and sustains health and well-being: An inte-
    grative, testable theory. Review of General Psychology
    2009; 13:242 <last_page> 251

30. Pinquart M: Creating and maintaining purpose in life in
    old age: A meta-analysis Ageing Int 2002; 27:90 <last_
    page> 114

31. Roe CM: Alzheimer disease and cognitive Reserve Vari-

ation of education effect with carbon 11–Labelled Pittsburgh compound B uptake Arch Neurol 2008; 65:1467

32. Ryff CD, Dienberg Love G, Urry HL, Muller D, Rosenkranz MA, Friedman EM, Davidson RJ, Singer B: Psychological well-being and ill-being: Do they have distinct or mirrored biological correlates? Psychother Psychosom 2006; 75:85-95

33. Ryff CD, Singer BH, Dienberg Love G: Positive health: Connecting well-being with biology Philos Trans R Soc Lond B Biol Sci 2004; 359:1383-1394

34. Ryff CD, Singer B: Psychological well-being: Meaning, measurement, and implications for psychotherapy research Psychother Psychosom 1996; 65:14 <last_page> 23

35. Scarmeas N, Stern Y: Cognitive reserve and lifestyle J. Clin Exp Neuropsychol 2003; 25:625-633

36. Scarmeas N: Association of life activities with cerebral blood flow in Alzheimer Disease Implications for the cognitive reserve hypothesis Arch Neurol 2003; 60:359

37. Stern Y: Cognitive reserved Neuropsychologia 2009; 47:2015 <last_page> 2028

38. Westerhof GJ, Bohlmeijer ET, van Beljouw IM, Pot AM: Improvement in personal meaning mediates the effects of a life review intervention on depressive symptoms in a randomized controlled trial Gerontologist 2010

39. Wilson RS, Schneider JA, Arnold SE, Bienias JL,

Bennett DA: Conscientiousness and the incidence of Alzheimer Disease and Mild Cognitive Impairment Arch Gen Psychiatry 2007; 64:1204-1212

40. Wood AM, Joseph S: The absence of positive psychological (eudemonic) well-being as a risk factor for depression: A ten year cohort study J Affect Disord 2010; 122:213 <last_page> 217

41. Boyle PAP, Buchman ASM, Wilson RSP, Yu LP, Schneider JAM, Bennett DAM: Effect of purpose in life on the relation between Alzheimer Disease pathological changes on cognitive function in advanced Age Purpose in life benefits for Alzheimer Disease. JAMA Network | Archives of General Psychiatry 2012; 69(5) 499-506

42. Jung CG: The Symbolic Life: Miscellaneous Writings, Volume 18. Princeton, N.J., Princeton University Press, 1976

43. Bedi A: Path to the Soul. York Beach, ME, S. Weiser, 2000

44. Jung CG: Collected Papers on Analytical Psychology. Kessinger Publishing, LLC, 2007

45. Lavretsky H: Resilience and Ageing: Research and Practice. Baltimore, Maryland, USA, Johns Hopkins University Press (22 August 2014)

46. Guirguis-Younger M, Grafanaki S: Narrative accounts of volunteers in palliative care settings. Am J Hosp Palliat Care 2008; 25:16-23

47. Jesuit Social Services, Parenting Australia: Soulmates:

A volunteer home visiting program for isolated sole parents : Final report. 2003

48. Klinedinst NJ, Resnick B: Volunteering and depressive symptoms among residents in a continuing care retirement community. J Gerontol Soc Work 2014; 57:52-71

49. Okulicz K: Try! A survival guide to unemployment. 1999; 64

50. Tullipan B, Carroll M, United States. Embassy, National Library of Australia: Ben tullipan interviewed by marg carroll in the resilient communities oral history project. 2012

51. Vaillant GE, Sobowale NC, McArthur C: Some Psychologic Vulnerabilities Of Physicians. The New England Journal Of Medicine 1972 Aug 24; 287:372-375

52. Bedi A: Crossing the Healing Zone—from Illness to Wellness. Lake Worth, FL, Nicholas-Hayes, Inc, 2013

53. Harris JC, DeAngelis CD: The power of hope JAMA 2008; 300:2919-2920

54. Weingarten K: Reasonable hope: Construct, clinical applications, and supports Fam Process 2010; 49:5-25

55. Griffith JL: Hope in cancer treatment, Psychiatric Annals 2014; 44:323-325

56. Edited by Snyder CR: Handbook of hope: Theory, measures, and applications. Edited by Anonymous New York, NY, Academic Press, 2000

57. Snyder CR, McDermott D, Cook J, Rapoff M: Hope

for the Journey: Helping Children through Good Times and Bad. Boulder, CO, Westview/Harper Collins, 1997

58. Foster C: Wired for God: The Biology of Spiritual Experience. Hodder & Stoughton, 2011

59. Hamer DH: the God Gene: How Faith is Hardwired into our Genes. Anchor Press, 2005

60. Alper M: the "God" Part of the Brain: A Scientific Interpretation of Human Spirituality and God, Source books, Inc., 2008

61. Waldman AN, Newberg A: how God Changes Your Brain: Breakthrough Findings from a Leading Neuro-scientist, Ballantine Books, 2009

62. Bruhn SW: the Power of Clan: The Influence of Human Relationships on Heart Disease. Transaction Publishers, 1998

63. Egolf B: "The roseto effect: A 50-year comparison of mortality rates," American Journal of Public Health, 1992; 82:1089-1092

64. Kark GS: "Does religious observance promote health? mortality in secular vs religious kibbutzim in Israel." American Journal of Public Health, 1996; 86:341-346

65. Randolph C, Byrd M: "Positive therapeutic effects of intercessory prayer in a coronary care unit population." Southern Medical Journal, 1988; 81:826-829

66. W.B.: the Language of the Heart in Bill W.S. Grapevine Writings. New York, The AA Grapevine Inc., 1988

67. Makinodan M, Rosen KM, Ito S, Corfas G: A critical period for social experience-dependent oligodendrocyte maturation and myelination Science 2012; 337:1357-1360

68. Long P, Corfas G: Dynamic regulation of myelination in health and disease JAMA Psychiatry 2014; 71:1296-1297

69. Bengtsson SL, Nagy Z, Skare S, Forsman L, Forssberg H, Ullén F: Extensive piano practicing has regionally specific effects on white matter development Nat Neurosci 2005; 2005; 8:1148 <last_page> 1150

70. Bedi A: Awaken the Slumbering Goddess–the Latent Code of the Hindu Goddess Archetypes. BookSurge, 2007

71. Jung CG, Shamdasani S, Hoerni U, Kyburz M, Peck J: The Red Book = Liber Novus. New York, W. W. Norton & Company, 2009

72. American/International Gita Society Bhagavad Gita 2013

73. Benson H, Stark M: Timeless Healing. USA, Scribner; Reprint edition, 1997

74. Luthar SS, Cicchetti D, Becker B: The construct of resilience: A critical evaluation and guidelines for future work. Child Dev., 2000; 71:543–562

75. Masten AS: Resilience processes in development. American Psychologist 2001; 56:227-238

76. Davidson RJ: Anxiety and affective style: Role of Pre-

frontal Cortex and Amygdala. Biol Psychiatry 2002; 51:68-80

77. Dalai Lama, Cutler HC: the Art of Happiness: A Handbook for Living. Hodder, 1998

78. Bonanno GA, Ho SMY, Chan JCK, Kwong RSY, Cheung CKY, Wong CPY, Wong VCW: Psychological resilience and dysfunction among hospitalized survivors of the SARS epidemic in hong kong: A latent class approach. Health Psychology 2008; 27:659 <last_page> 667

79. Charney DS: Psychobiological mechanisms of resilience and vulnerability: Implications for successful adaptation to extreme stress Am J Psychiatry 2004; 161:195 <last_page> 216

80. Davidson RJ: Affective style, psychopathology, and resilience: Brain mechanisms and plasticity. Am Psychol 2000; 55:1196 <last_page> 1214

81. James LM: Neural network modulation by trauma as a marker of Resilience Differences between veterans with Post-Traumatic Stress Disorder and Resilient Controls Neural network modulation and resilience JAMA Psychiatry 2013; 1

82. King LA, King DW, Vogt DS, Knight J, Samper RE: Deployment risk and resilience inventory: A collection of measures for studying deployment-related experiences of military personnel and veterans. Mil Psychol 2006; 18:89 <last_page> 120

83. McEwen BS: Interacting mediators of allostasis and allostatic load: Towards an understanding of resilience in aging Metab Clin Exp 2003; 52:10 <last_page> 16

84. Waugh CE, Wager TD, Fredrickson BL, Noll DC, Taylor SF: The neural correlates of trait resilience when anticipating and recovering from threat Social Cognitive and Affective Neuroscience 2008; 3:322 <last_page> 332

85. van der Kolk B: the Body Keeps the Score: Brain, Mind, and Body in the Healing of Trauma. Viking Adult, 2014

86. van der Kolk B: Yoga as an adjunctive treatemnt for PTSD. The Journal of Clinical Psychiatry 2014; 75:559-565

87. LeDoux J: Rethinking the emotional brain. Neuron 2012; 73:653-676

88. LeDoux JE: Brain mechanisms of emotion and emotional learning. Curr Opin Neurobiol 1992; 2:191-197

89. LeDoux JE: Emotion circuits in the brain Annu Rev Neurosci 2000; 23:155-184

90. McDonald AJ: Cortical pathways to the mammalian amygdala. Prog Neurobiol 1998; 55:257-332

91. Milad MR, Wright CI, Orr SP, Pitman RK, Quirk GJ, Rauch SL: Recall of fear extinction in humans activates the ventromedial prefrontal cortex and hippocampus in concert. Biol Psychiatry 2007; 62:446-454

92. Morgan MA, Schulkin J, LeDoux JE: Ventral medial prefrontal cortex and emotional perseveration: The

memory for prior extinction training. Behav Brain Res 2003; 146:121-130

93. Motzkin JC, Philippi CL, Wolf RC, Baskaya MK, Koenigs M: Ventromedial prefrontal cortex is critical for the regulation of amygdala activity in humans. Biol Psychiatry

94. Phan KL, Taylor SF, Welsh RC, Decker LR, Noll DC, Nichols TE, Britton JC, Liberzon I: Activation of the medial prefrontal cortex and extended amygdala by individual ratings of emotional arousal: A fMRI study. Biol Psychiatry 2003; 53:211-215

95. Phelps EA, Delgado MR, Nearing KI, LeDoux JE: Extinction learning in humans: Role of the amygdala and vmPFC. Neuron 2004; 43:897-905

96. Phelps EA: Emotion and cognition: Insights from studies of the human amygdala Annu Rev Psychol 2006; 57:27 <last_page> 53

97. Rauch SL, Shin LM, Phelps EA: Neurocircuitry models of posttraumatic stress disorder and extinction: Human neuroimaging Research—Past, present, and future. Biol Psychiatry 2006; 60:376-382

98. Sotres-Bayon F., Quirk GJ: Prefrontal control of fear: More than just extinction. Curr Opin Neurobiol 2010; 20:231-235

99. Siegel DJ: Mindsight: The New Science of Personal Transformation. USA, Bantam, 2010

100. Siegel DJ: the Mindful Brain: Reflection and Attune-

ment in the Cultivation of Well-being. New York, NY, W. W. Norton & Company, 2007

101.   Black C, Bucky SF, Wilder-Padilla S: International journal of addictions, The Interpersonal and Emotional Consequences of being an Adult Child of an Alcoholic 21(2) (1986): pp 213-31

102.   Parker DA, Harford TC: Journal of studies on alcohol, Alcohol-Related Problems, Marital Disruption and Depressive Symptoms among Adult Children of Alcohol Abusers in the United States" 1988; 49(4):pp 306-13

103.   Wegscheider S: another Chance: Hope and Health for Alcoholic Families. Palo Alto, Science and Behavior Books, 1981

104.   Edited by Lindsay K.C., Vergo P.: Kandinsky: Complete writings on art, Edited by Anonymous Boston, GK Hall, 1982

105.   Buckley P.J.: Wassily kandinsky, 1866–1944: American journal of psychiatry: The American Journal of Psychiatry 2014; Vol 171:1054-1055

106.   Gregoire C: The unexpected source that inspired whole foods, apple's sleek design and the white album The Huffington Post 2013

107.   Jung CG: Psychological Types, Volume 6. London, Routledge & Kegan Paul, 1981

108.   Chopra D: Perfect Health: The Complete Mindbody Guide. London, Bantam, 2001

109.   Perlmutter D: Grain Brain: The Surprising Truth about

Wheat, Carbs, and Sugar—Your Brain's Silent Killers. New York, Boston, London, Little, Brown and Company; (17 September 2013)

110. Cahill GFJ, Veech Richard L.: Ketoacids? good medicine? 2003; v 114

111. Ahmadi N., Eshaghian S., Huizenga R., Sosnin K., Ebrahimi R., Siegel R.: Effects of intense exercise and moderate caloric restriction on cardiovascular risk factors and inflammation. Am J Med 2011; 124:978-982

112. Ahmet I, Tae H, de Cabo R, Lakatta EG, Talan MI: Effects of calorie restriction on cardioprotection and cardiovascular health. J Mol Cell Cardiol 2011; 51:263-271

113. Ahmet I., Wan R., Iyun T., Krawczyk M., Mattson MP, Lakatta EG, Talan MI: Cardioprotective potential of intermittent fasting in rats. J Card Fail 2004; 10:S89

114. Anton S, Leeuwenburgh C: Fasting or caloric restriction for healthy aging. Exp Gerontol 2013; 48:1003-1005

115. Azevedo FRd, Ikeoka D, Caramelli B: Effects of intermittent fasting on metabolism in men. Revista Da Associação Médica Brasileira 2013; 59:167-173

116. Aziz AR, Slater GJ, Chia MYH, Teh KC: Effects of ramadan fasting on training induced adaptations to a seven-week high-intensity interval exercise program. Science & Sports 2012; 27:31-38

117. BaHammam A, Alrajeh M, Albabtain M, Bahammam

S, Sharif M: Circadian pattern of sleep, energy expenditure, and body temperature of young healthy men during the intermittent fasting of ramadan. Appetite 2010; 54:426-429

118. Bouhlel E, Salhi Z, Bouhlel H, Mdella S, Amamou A, Zaouali M, Mercier J, Bigard X, Tabka Z, Zbidi A, Shephard R: Effect of ramadan fasting on fuel oxidation during exercise in trained male rugby players. Diabetes Metab 2006; 32:617-624

119. Carlson O, Martin B, Stote KS, Golden E, Maudsley S, Najjar SS, Ferrucci L, Ingram DK, Longo DL, Rumpler WV, Baer DJ, Egan J, Mattson MP: Impact of reduced meal frequency without caloric restriction on glucose regulation in healthy, normal-weight middle-aged men and women. Metab Clin Exp 2007; 56:1729-1734

120. Castello L, Froio T, Maina M, Cavallini G, Biasi F, Leonarduzzi G, Donati A, Bergamini E, Poli G, Chiarpotto E: Alternate-day fasting protects the rat heart against age-induced inflammation and fibrosis by inhibiting oxidative damage and NF-kB activation. Free Radical Biology and Medicine 2010; 48:47-54

121. Descamps O, Riondel J, Ducros V, Roussel A: Mitochondrial production of reactive oxygen species and incidence of age-associated lymphoma in OF1 mice: Effect of alternate-day fasting. Mech Ageing Dev 2005; 126:1185-1191

122. Faris AE, Kacimi S, Al-Kurd RA, Fararjeh MA, Bustanji YK, Mohammad MK, Salem ML: Intermittent fasting

during ramadan attenuates proinflammatory cytokines and immune cells in healthy subjects. Nutr Res 2012; 32:947-955

123. Fond G, Macgregor A, Leboyer M, Michalsen A: Fasting in mood disorders: Neurobiology and effectiveness. A review of the literature. Psychiatry Res 2013; 209:253-258

124. Goodrick CL, Ingram DK, Reynolds MA, Freeman JR, Cider N: Effects of intermittent feeding upon body weight and lifespan in inbred mice: Interaction of genotype and age. Mech Ageing Dev 1990; 55:69-87

125. Hartman AL, Rubenstein JE, Kossoff EH: Intermittent fasting: A "new" historical strategy for controlling seizures? Epilepsy Res 2013; 104:275-279

126. Holloszy JO, Fontana L: Caloric restriction in humans. Exp Gerontol 2007; 42:709-712

127. Johnson JB, John S, Laub DR: Pretreatment with alternate day modified fast will permit higher dose and frequency of cancer chemotherapy and better cure rates. Med Hypotheses 2009; 72:381-382

128. Johnson JB, Laub DR, John S: The effect on health of alternate day calorie restriction: Eating less and more than needed on alternate days prolongs life. Med Hypotheses 2006; 67:209-211

129. Long P, Nguyen Q, Thurow C, Broderick TL: Caloric restriction restores the cardioprotective effect of preconditioning in the rat heart. Mech Ageing Dev 2002; 123:1411-1413

130. Longo V, Mattson M: Fasting: Molecular mechanisms and clinical applications. Cell Metabolism 2014; 19:181-192

131. Maalouf M, Rho JM, Mattson MP: The neuroprotective properties of calorie restriction, the ketogenic diet, and ketone bodies. Brain Res Rev 2009; 59:293-315

132. Martin B, Mattson MP, Maudsley S: Caloric restriction and intermittent fasting: Two potential diets for successful brain aging. Ageing Research Reviews 2006; 5:332-353

133. Masoro EJ: Caloric restriction-induced life extension of rats and mice: A critique of proposed mechanisms. Biochimica Et Biophysica Acta (BBA) - General Subjects 2009; 1790:1040-1048

134. Masoro EJ: Overview of caloric restriction and ageing. Mech Ageing Dev 2005; 126:913-922

135. Masoro EJ: Caloric restriction and aging: An update. Exp Gerontol 2000; 35:299-305

136. Mattson MP, Wan T, Ruiqian.: Beneficial effects of intermittent fasting and caloric restriction on the cardiovascular and cerebrovascular systems The Journal of Nutritional Biochemistry March 2005, Pages; 16:129-137

137. Mattson MP: Neuroprotective signaling and the aging brain: Take away my food and let me run. Brain Res 2000; 886:47-53

138. Mattson MP, Duan W, Maswood N: How does the

brain control lifespan? Ageing Research Reviews 2002; 1:155-165

139. Mattson MP, Maudsley S, Martin B: BDNF and 5-HT: A dynamic duo in age-related neuronal plasticity and neurodegenerative disorders. Trends Neurosci 2004; 27:589-594

140. McCarty MF, Falahati-Nini A: Neuroprotective potential of the bahadori leanness program: A "mini-fast with exercise" strategy. Med Hypotheses 2007; 68:935-940

141. Melo ES, de Azevedo FR, Monteiro LH, Caramelli B: 702 Intermittent Fasting: Physiological Data Regarding A New Approach For The Nutritional Prevention Of Atherosclerosis. Atherosclerosis Supplements 2011; 12:147-148

142. Mercken EM, Carboneau BA, Krzysik-Walker SM, de Cabo R: Of mice and men: The benefits of caloric restriction, exercise, and mimetics. Ageing Research Reviews 2012; 11:390-398

143. Mulas MF, Demuro G, Mulas C, Putzolu M, Cavallini G, Donati A, Bergamini E, Dessi S: Dietary restriction counteracts age-related changes in cholesterol metabolism in the rat. Mech Ageing Dev 2005; 126:648-654

144. Nørrelund H: The metabolic role of growth hormone in humans with particular reference to fasting. Growth Hormone & IGF Research 2005; 15:95-122

145. Pijl H: Longevity. the allostatic load of dietary restriction. Physiol Behav 2012; 106:51-57

146. Redman LM, Martin CK, Williamson DA, Ravussin E: Effect of caloric restriction in non-obese humans on physiological, psychological and behavioral outcomes. Physiol Behav 2008; 94:643-648

147. Roth LW, Polotsky AJ: Can we live longer by eating less? A review of caloric restriction and longevity. Maturitas 2012; 71:315-319

148. Sogawa H, Kubo C: Influence of short-term repeated fasting on the longevity of female (NZB×NZW)F1 mice. Mech Ageing Dev 2000; 115:61-71

149. Teng NIMF, Shahar S, Manaf ZA, Das SK, Taha CSC, Ngah WZW: Efficacy of fasting calorie restriction on quality of life among aging men. Physiol Behav 2011; 104:1059-1064

150. Weindruch R: Caloric restriction: Life span extension and retardation of brain aging. Clinical Neuroscience Research 2003; 2:279-284

151. Vaynman S, Ying Z, Gomez-Pinilla F: Hippocampal BDNF mediates the efficacy of exercise on synaptic plasticity and cognition Eur J. Neurosci 2004; 20:2580 <last_page> 2590

152. Holmes MM, Galea LA, Mistlberger RE, Kempermann G: Adult hippocampal neurogenesis and voluntary running activity: Circadian and dose-dependent effects J Neurosci Res 2004; 76:216-222

153. Li L, Men WW, Chang YK, Fan MX, Ji L, Wei GX: Acute aerobic exercise increases cortical activity during

working memory: A functional MRI study in female college students. PLoS One 2014; 9:e99222

154. Moser MB, Moser EI, Forrest E, Andersen P, Morris RG: Spatial learning with a minislab in the dorsal hippocampus Proceedings of the National Academy of Sciences 1995; 92:9697 <last_page> 9701

155. Pang PT: Cleavage of proBDNF by tPA/Plasmin is essential for long-term hippocampal plasticity Science 2004; 306:487 <last_page> 491

156. Redila VA, Christie BR: Exercise-induced changes in dendritic structure and complexity in the adult hippocampal dentate gyrus Neuroscience 2006; 137:1299 <last_page> 1307

157. Coen RF, Lawlor BA, Kenny R: Failure to demonstrate that memory improvement is due either to aerobic exercise or increased hippocampal volume Proc Natl Acad Sci USA 2011; 108:E89; author reply E90

158. Czeh B, Michaelis T, Watanabe T, Frahm J, de Biurrun G, van Kampen M, Bartolomucci A, Fuchs E: Stress-induced changes in cerebral metabolites, hippocampal volume, and cell proliferation are prevented by antidepressant treatment with tianeptine Proc Natl Acad Sci U S A 2001; 98:12796-12801

159. Eisch AJ, Barrot M, Schad CA, Self DW, Nestler EJ: Opiates inhibit neurogenesis in the adult rat hippocampus Proc Natl Acad Sci U S A 2000; 97:7579-7584

160. Erickson KI, Prakash RS, Voss MW, Chaddock L,

Hu L, Morris KS, White SM, Wojcicki TR, McAuley E, Kramer AF: Aerobic fitness is associated with hippocampal volume in elderly humans Hippocampus 2009; 19:1030-1039

161. Erickson KI, Voss MW, Prakash RS, Basak C, Szabo A, Chaddock L, Kim JS, Heo S, Alves H, White SM, Wojcicki TR, Mailey E, Vieira VJ, Martin SA, Pence BD, Woods JA, McAuley E, Kramer AF: Exercise training increases size of hippocampus and improves memory Proceedings of the National Academy of Sciences 2011; 2011; 108:3017 <last_page> 3022

162. Cotman C: Exercise: A behavioral intervention to enhance brain health and plasticity Trends Neurosci 2002; 25:295 <last_page> 301

163. Bauman AE, Bellew B, Owen N, Vita P: Impact of an australian mass media campaign targeting physical activity in 1998. Am J Prev Med 2001; 21:41-47

164. Baxter A, JP Francis A: Positive impact of tai chi chuan participation on biopsychosocial quality of life compared to exercise and sedentary controls: A cross-sectional survey. J Complement Integr Med 2013; 10:10.1515/jcim-2012-0008

165. Black JE, Isaacs KR, Anderson BJ, Alcantara AA, Greenough WT: Learning causes synaptogenesis, whereas motor activity causes angiogenesis, in cerebellar cortex of adult rats. Proceedings of the National Academy of Sciences 1990; 87:5568 <last_page> 5572

166. Bogaert I, De Martelaer K, Deforche B, Clarys P, Zinzen E: Associations between different types of physical activity and teachers' perceived mental, physical, and work-related health. BMC Public Health 2014; 14:534

167. Chu AH, Koh D, Moy FM, Muller-Riemenschneider F: Do workplace physical activity interventions improve mental health outcomes? Occup Med (Lond) 2014; 64:235-245

168. Colcombe S, Kramer AF: Fitness effects on the cognitive function of older adults: A meta-analytic study Psychological Science 2003; 14:125 <last_page> 130

169. Erickson KI, Raji CA, Lopez OL, Becker JT, Rosano C, Newman AB, Gach HM, Thompson PM, Ho AJ, Kuller LH: Physical activity predicts gray matter volume in late adulthood: The cardiovascular health study Neurology 2010; 75:1415-1422

170. Hillman CH, Erickson KI, Kramer AF: Be smart, exercise your heart: Exercise effects on brain and cognition Nature Reviews Neuroscience 2008; 9:58 <last_page> 65

171. Kramer AF, Hahn S, Cohen NJ, Banich MT, McAuley E, Harrison CR, Chason J, Vakil E, Bardell L, Boileau RA, Colcombe A: Ageing, fitness and neurocognitive function Nature 1999; 400:418-419

172. Landi F, Russo A, Bernabei R: Physical activity and behavior in the elderly: A pilot study. Arch Gerontol Geriatr Suppl 2004; (9):235-241

173. Li JX, Hong Y, Chan KM: Tai chi: Physiological characteristics and beneficial effects on health. Br J Sports Med 2001; 35:148-156

174. Neeper SA, Gomez-Pinilla F, Choi J, Cotman C: Exercise and brain neurotrophins Nature 1995; 373:109

175. Pereira AC, Huddleston DE, Brickman AM, Sosunov AA, Hen R, McKhann GM, Sloan R, Gage FH, Brown TR, Small SA: An in vivo correlate of exercise-induced neurogenesis in the adult dentate gyrus Proceedings of the National Academy of Sciences 2007; 2007; 104:5638 <last_page> 5643

176. Smith PJ, Blumenthal JA, Hoffman BM, Cooper H, Strauman TA, Welsh-Bohmer K, Browndyke JN, Sherwood A: Aerobic exercise and neurocognitive performance: A meta-analytic review of randomized controlled trials Psychosom Med 2010; 72:239-252

177. Williamson JD, Espeland M, Kritchevsky SB, Newman AB, King AC, Pahor M, Guralnik JM, Pruitt LA, Miller ME, LIFE Study Investigators: Changes in cognitive function in a randomized trial of physical activity: Results of the lifestyle interventions and independence for elders pilot study. J Gerontol A Biol Sci Med Sci 2009; 64:688-694

178. Taheri S, Lin L, Austin D, Young T, Mignot. Emmanuel: Short sleep duration is associated with reduced leptin, elevated ghrelin, and increased body mass index. PLOS Medicine 2004 December; 1:210-217

179. Alam M, Barrett KC, Hodapp RM, Arndt KA: Botulinum toxin and the facial feedback hypothesis: Can looking better make you feel happier? J Am Acad Dermatol 2008; 58:1061-1072

180. Davis JI, Senghas A, Ochsner KN: How does facial feedback modulate emotional experience? Journal of Research in Personality 2009; 43:822-829

181. Heckmann M, Teichmann B, Schröder U, Sprengelmeyer R, Ceballos-Baumann AO: Pharmacologic denervation of frown muscles enhances baseline expression of happiness and decreases baseline expression of anger, sadness, and fear. J Am Acad Dermatol 2003; 49:213-216

182. Joshua CA: "Humor and Oncology," Journal of Clinical Oncology, 2005; 23:645-648

183. Penson PR: "Laughter: The best medicine? Oncologist 2005; 10:651-660

184. Seaward BL: "Humor's healing potential." Health Programs 1992; 73:66-70

185. Weisenberg MTI: "Humor as a cognitive technique for increasing pain tolerance," Pain 1995; 63:207-212

186. Ziegler J: "Immune system may benefit from the ability to laugh." Journal of the National Cancer Institute, Oxford University Press 1995; 87:342-343

187. Brizer DA, Castaneda R: Clinical Addiction Psychiatry. Cambridge, Cambridge University Press, 2010

188. Dias BG, Ressler KJ: Parental olfactory experience

influences behavior and neural structure in subsequent generations. Nature Neuroscience 2014; 17:89-96

189. Kaliman P, Alvarez-Lopez MJ, Cosin-Tomas M, Rosenkranz MA, Lutz A, Davidson RJ: Rapid changes in histone deacetylases and inflammatory gene expression in expert meditators. Psychoneuroendocrinology 2014; 40:96-107

190. Carlson LE, Beattie TL, Giese-Davis J, Faris P, Tamagawa R, Fick LJ, Degelman ES, Speca M: Mindfulness-based cancer recovery and supportive-expressive therapy maintain telomere length relative to controls in distressed breast cancer survivors. Cancer 2015; 121:476-484

191. Epel E, Daubenmier J, Moskowitz JT, Folkman S, Blackburn E: Can meditation slow rate of cellular aging? cognitive stress, mindfulness, and telomeres. Ann NY Acad Sci 2009; 1172:34-53

192. Falus A, Marton I, Borbenyi E, Tahy A, Karadi P, Aradi J, Stauder A, Kopp M: The 2009 nobel prize in medicine and its surprising message: Lifestyle is associated with telomerase activity. Orv Hetil 2010; 151:965-970

193. Hoge EA, Chen MM, Orr E, Metcalf CA, Fischer LE, Pollack MH, De Vivo I, Simon NM: Loving-kindness meditation practice associated with longer telomeres in women. Brain Behav Immun 2013; 32:159-163

194. Jacobs TL, Epel ES, Lin J, Blackburn EH, Wolkowitz OM, Bridwell DA, Zanesco AP, Aichele SR, Sahdra

BK, MacLean KA, King BG, Shaver PR, Rosenberg EL, Ferrer E, Wallace BA, Saron CD: Intensive meditation training, immune cell telomerase activity, and psychological mediators. Psychoneuroendocrinology 2011; 36:664-681

195. Schutte NS, Malouff JM: A meta-analytic review of the effects of mindfulness meditation on telomerase activity. Psychoneuroendocrinology 2014; 42:45-48

196. Stefano GB, Fricchione GL, Slingsby BT, Benson H: The placebo effect and relaxation response: Neural processes and their coupling to constitutive nitric oxide. Brain Research Reviews 2001; 35:1-19

197. Jung CG: Symbols of Transformation: An Analysis of the Prelude to a Case of Schizophrenia, Volume 5. Princeton, N.J., Princeton University Press, 1956

198. Jung CG: the Red Book: Liber Novus, Edited and Introduced by Sonu Shamdasani, New York and London, W.W. Norton and Company, 2009

199. Saint A: Confessions (Works of Saint Augustine: A Translation for the 21st Century). New York, http://www.amazon.com/s/ref=dp_byline_sr_book_1?ie=UT-F8&field-author=Saint+Augustine&search-alias=books & text=Saint+Augustine & sort=relevancerank, 1996.

Retire Your Family Karma
Decode Your Family Pattern and Find Your Soul Path
Ashok Bedi, M.D. & Boris Matthews, Ph.D.

We reap what we sow, but we also reap what others before us have sown. If we do this unconsciously, we find ourselves victims of unfortunate circumstances, but if we are conscious of what we have taken on from our family legacy, we can turn it around.

Doctors Bedi and Matthews have worked with people who have carried the burden of their families, best achievements, worst failures, and unrealized dreams. With their experience, we learn to recognize our karmic inheritance and settle our family?s karmic accounts so we can redirect our energies in accord with our own true path and passion, our soul's calling. Bedi and Matthews explain how ancestral karma gets energetically encoded in the chakras of our subtle body and manifests as chakra blockages or overactivity. .

To totally comprehend our roots and to realize our destiny, we must look beyond our individual life and understand our ancestral context in order to make sense of our journey. ... Once we have identified the blessings and the curses we have inherited, we have the possibility of choice. The best way to break old patterns is to work on establishing new ones.

192 pp. • 7 illustrations • 5 ½ x 8 ½ • ISBN: 978-0-89254-081-5
Paperback • $18.95

Crossing the Healing Zone
From Illness to Wellness
Ashok Bedi, M.D.

The medicine of the 20th century was about the treatment of illness. The medicine of the 21st century is about wellness. *Crossing the Healing Zone* advances the new concepts of the emerging frontiers of integrative medicine, bringing together Eastern and Western healing traditions and merging body, mind, and spirit in a Jungian perspective.

The journey through the Healing Zone that Dr. Bedi proposes is guided by archetypes and myths, active imagination, dreams and synchronicities, and the neuroplastic mysteries of our complex physical reality. The book contains informative and visual guidelines and practices that can help us create and manage our own personal wellness programs and become full and active partners in our own journeys from illness to wellness.

"Dr. Bedi is uniquely equipped to bring together the best of contemporary medicine, depth psychology, modern physics and ancient religious traditions in a highly practical and useful way.." —Murray Stein, Ph.D., author of *Jung's Map of the Soul*

244 pp. • 6 x 9 • ISBN: 978-0-89254-203-1 • eISBN: 978-0-89254-589-6 • Paperback • $21.95